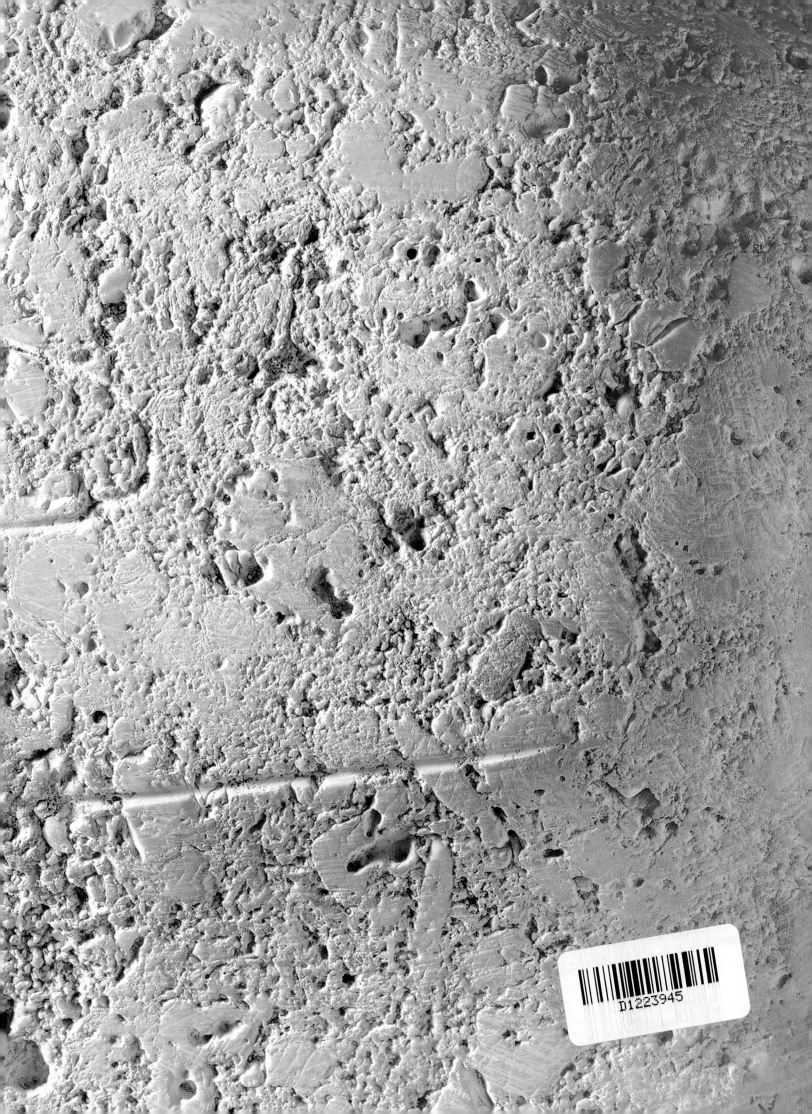

SPECIALISTS AND SERVICES FOR THIS AUCTION

For assistance and further information about this sale, please contact the following on Tel: +1 212 636 2050 or Fax: +1 212 636 2035

SPECIALISTS FOR THE SALE, NEW YORK

Guy Bennett
International Co-
Head of Department

Thomas Seydoux
International Co-
Head of Department

Cyanne Chutkow
Senior Specialist

Conor Jordan
Senior Specialist

Sharon Kim
Senior Specialist

Liz Clark
Associate Specialist

Brooke Lampley
Associate Specialist

Stefany Sekara
Associate Specialist

Jessica Fertig
Junior Specialist

Amy Albright
Expertise

Maxwell Carter
Cataloguer/
Researcher

SPECIALISTS FOR THE SALE, EUROPE

Jussi Pylkkänen

Andreas Rumbler

Giovanna
Bertazonni

Matthew
Stephenson

Anika Guntrum

Christopher Burge
Honorary Chairman,
America

John Lumley
Vice-Chairman,
Europe

Ken Yeh
Deputy Chairman,
Asia

Sheri Farber
International Client
Developement
Director

SERVICES

ABSENTEE AND TELEPHONE BIDS
Tel: +1 212 636 2437
Fax: +1 212 636 4938
Internet: www.christies.com

AUCTION RESULTS
US: +1 212 703 8080
UK: +44 (0)20 7627 2707
Internet: www.christies.com

CATALOGUES ONLINE
Lotfinder®
Internet: www.christies.com

INSURANCE
Tel: +1 212 636 2353
Fax: +1 212 492 4947

PAYMENT
Buyers
Tel: +1 212 636 2495
Fax: +1 212 636 4939
Consignors
Tel: +1 212 636 2350
Fax: +1 212 492 5477

ART TRANSPORT
Tel: +1 212 636 2480
Fax: +1 212 636 4937

STORAGE AND COLLECTION
Tel: +1 212 636 2495
Fax: +1 212 636 4939

christies.com

AUCTION ADMINISTRATOR
Jenna Filia
Tel: +1 212 636 2639
Fax: +1 212 636 2035

INTERNATIONAL BUSINESS DIRECTOR
Jennifer Zatorksi
Tel: +1 212 468 7148
Fax: +1 212 636 4932

Senior Writer and Researcher
John Steinert

We thank Abby McEwen for her assistance in researching and preparing notes for various lots in this catalogue.

THE ENERGY AND POWER OF GREAT MOUNTAINS HENRY MOORE

IMPRESSIONIST/MODERN EVENING SALE

THURSDAY 6 NOVEMBER 2008

AUCTION

Thursday 6 November 2008
at 6.30 pm

20 Rockefeller Plaza
New York, NY 10020

Admission to this sale is by ticket only. Please call +1 212 636 2437
for further information.

VIEWING

Thursday	30 October	12.00 pm – 5.00 pm
Friday	31 October	10.00 am – 5.00 pm
Saturday	1 November	10.00 am – 5.00 pm
Sunday	2 November	1.00 pm – 5.00 pm
Monday	3 November	10.00 am – 5.00 pm
Tuesday	4 November	10.00 am – 2.00 pm

AUCTIONEER

Christopher Burge (# 761543)

AUCTION CODE AND NUMBER

In sending absentee bids or making
enquiries, this sale should be referred to as
ROCCO–2045

AUCTION RESULTS

UK: +44 (0)20 7627 2707
US: +1 212 703 8080
christies.com

CONDITIONS OF SALE

This auction is subject to
Important Notices,
Conditions of Sale and
to reserves.
[60]

This auction features
CHRISTIE'S LIVE
Bid live in Christie's salerooms worldwide

register at **www.christies.com**

CHRISTIE'S

View catalogues and leave bids online
at **christies.com**

CONTENTS

2   Specialists and Services for this Auction

3   Auction Information

6   Property for Sale

74   Christie's International Impressionist, 20th Century
and Contemporary Department

75   Christie's International Impressionist, 20th Century
and Contemporary Auction Calendar

76   Important Notices and Explanation of Cataloguing Practice

77   Buying at Christie's

78   Storage and Collection

79   Conditions of Sale and Limited Warranty

81   Salerooms and Offices Worldwide

83   Christie's Specialist Departments and Services

85   Absentee Bids Form

86   Catalogue Subscriptions

FRONT COVER:
Lot 14

BACK COVER:
Lot 62

INSIDE COVERS:
Lot 14

All images reproduced by permission of the
Henry Moore Foundation

THE ENERGY AND POWER OF GREAT MOUNTAINS

EIGHT SCULPTURES BY HENRY MOORE

BY JOHN STEINERT

On 2 November, while the sale viewing for the sculptures in this catalogue is in progress, an important exhibition of related interest will close: *Moore in America*, at The New York Botanical Garden in the Bronx. Moore declared, "Sculpture is an art of the open air. Daylight, sunlight is necessary to it, and for me the best setting and complement is nature. I would rather have a piece of my sculpture put in a landscape, almost any landscape, than in, or on, the most beautiful building I know." This is the most extensive open-air exhibition of Henry Moore's sculpture ever held in the United States, featuring twenty monumental works in bronze and fiberglass which have been installed on the grounds of a beautiful 250-acre natural and cultivated public space, the largest in any American city. The sculptures will then travel to the Atlanta Botanical Garden in spring 2009. Another major show was held last year at the Royal Botanic Gardens in Kew; this was the first outdoor display of Moore's large sculptures in Great Britain in more than twenty years. Since the year 2000 there have been notable exhibitions of Moore's work around the world, in Finland, France, Germany, Greece, Mexico, Brazil, Japan and China.

Moore in America is a timely reminder of Henry Moore's significance as the one of the leading sculptors of the 20th century. I say "one of...," there are others who would declare outright that he is surely the greatest of his time. One can indeed make a strong argument for this claim. Neverthless, I do not hesitate to place Alberto Giacometti in the same league, and I find it instructive to take the measure of both men and contrast their work to arrive at the fullest appreciation of the ideas and expression which modern sculpture communicates to us. I am grateful to have seen the important retrospective of Giacometti's work at The Museum of Modern Art, New York in 2001, and the smaller but no less striking show *The Women of Giacometti* at Pace/Wildenstein, New York in 2005. North Americans interested in Moore can visit sizable collections of the sculptor's work at the Hirshhorn Museum and Sculpture Garden in Washington, D.C.; The Nelson-Atkins Museum of Art in Kansas City, Missouri; and the Art Gallery of Ontario, Toronto, which in fact houses the largest public collection of Moore's sculptures anywhere in the world. Nonetheless, I am disappointed not to have had the opportunity, during my adult lifetime, to attend a comprehensive retrospective of Moore's work in or around New York. While the outdoor display in the Bronx is certainly a memorable event, and the sculptures there trace most of the major themes in Moore's work, it is, as Anita Feldman, the Curator of the Henry Moore Foundation, readily points out, "not a retrospective," for the reason that it "naturally excludes a vast amount of material—it does not embrace the artist's carvings or works on paper..."

It may well be that a definitive Moore retrospective is a logistical impossibility—the sheer scope and the actual physical size of much of his work would preclude such an event. It should be possible, however, to undertake a major exhibition in which a large number of works are selected from a narrower context, taking a particular theme or period as a point of reference. First preference on my list would be a show of the early sculptures, from the 1920s and 30s, seen perhaps in the context of works by other artists of the period and with the sculptures from earlier times and other cultures which influenced them. My British colleagues are partial to the early sculptures, which are hardly known to Americans. The early surrealist works in the 2001 Giacometti MoMA retrospective were unforgettable; they completely reshaped my understanding of Giacometti's work. Moore's early work comes out of a similar milieu, and I am sure the their impact would be no less startling and memorable.

There are eight sculptures by Moore in this catalogue. Christie's makes no pretense to this group being an absolute representation—our specialists have to work within an especially pressing set of conditions when bringing such work together, and within a very short space of time. Nonetheless, each work in this group possesses singular and remarkable qualities, and together they will surely make a strong showing—indeed, I look forward to the day when the sale viewing opens and each of these impressive works can finally be seen within the proximity and context of the others.

There are two rarely encountered early sculptures, I am glad to see, both simply titled *Figure*: one a primitive carved wood piece from 1932, and the other the important Figure, 1933-1934, with its famous hole, a key work in Moore's development. There is a war-time four-member *Family Group*, 1944, the perennial favorite among the sculptor's themes. *Working Model for Seated Woman*, 1980, has a sibylline, oracular presence. As befitting Moore's most numerous, signature subject, there are three very different reclining women, the abstract *Reclining Figure: External Form*, 1953-1954; the black granite *Two Piece Reclining Figure: Armless*, 1977; and the autumnal and deeply sensual *Reclining Woman: Elbow*, 1981, which is arguably Moore's final masterpiece. Most mysterious of all is the sleekly minimal, yet richly evocative *Arch Form*, 1970, in black marble.

The large sculptures in this group would be perfectly at home in the landscape setting of the Bronx Botanical Garden. It is perhaps Moore's greatest contribution to modern sculpture to re-envision the human body as landscape, to correlate natural forms with all aspects of our bodily structure and appearance. We are, of course, nature, even if our philosophy, religion, social imperatives and our very consciousness—in all its egotistical superiority—does everything in their power to isolate us from nature, while at the same time compelling us to brutally and carelessly subjugate it. Having been driven from the garden, Moore bids us to return and enter it. We exist in the world, he tells us, we exist in the very image of the world, and the world exists in us.

Giacometti sought to create a pure and irreducible presence in his figures, a stillness and finality which sends a shiver of recognition down our spine, so that we seem to be looking deeply into the most fragile and vulnerable recesses of our selves, fraught as we are with apprehension and anxiety. He was the sculptor of people who dwell in cities, who walk the streets of any metropolis, moving within the constraint of tight, inward pressing spaces. Moore, on the other hand, wanted to draw us out of the singularity of self by which we normally define our identity, and his work urges us to open our consciousness to widening circles of transformation and multiplicity. He is the pastoral sculptor par excellence, whose forms follow the curvature of the landscape, the flow of a river, the growth of plants—his forms are fluid, Protean, but nonetheless powerful, enduring and serene. Time seems to stand still in his work—we may read in these forms the elemental and eternal cycles of life and death, as the ancients knew and accepted it, and we can trace the deepening furrows of the endless passing of seasons. Moore said: "The whole of nature—bones, pebbles, shells, clouds, tree trunks, flowers—all is grist to the mill of a sculpture... It's a question of metamorphosis. We must relate the human figure to animals, to clouds, to the landscape—bring them all together. There's no difference. By using them like metaphors in poetry, you give new meaning to things."

In its pursuit of pure form—form which exists only in and for itself, expressing none other than itself—modernism is not normally conducive to creating metaphors, which is a romantic or even medieval function of the creative imagination, an intuitive process by which one thing suggests another in a string of continuous and revelatory association. Picasso could create metaphors in his sculpture, or perhaps they are more simply similes, because in his use of assemblage he often makes astonishing statements that tend to be brashly clever rather than contemplative and profound. Among the moderns the Surrealists prized and exalted the gift for poetic metaphor, and the love of plastic metaphor in Moore's work probably stems in part from his early encounter with Surrealism. More importantly, there may be some natural propensity in the English or Celtic character to readily think, imagine and seek expression in metaphor; this is the very basis and splendor of English poetry. I think of Moore, in this respect, as heir to the great poets of the 19th century, working in stone or wood instead of words. I suspect that Moore would have gladly found himself among kindred spirits if he could have wandered the hills and dales of the Lake District with Coleridge, Southey, and especially Wordsworth:

THE CATARACTS BLOW THEIR TRUMPETS FROM THE STEEP,

NO MORE SHALL GRIEF OF MINE THE SEASON WRONG;

I HEAR THE ECHOES THROUGH THE MOUNTAINS THRONG,

THE WINDS COME TO ME FROM THE FIELDS OF SLEEP,

AND ALL THE EARTH IS GAY...

This poetic function connects easily with myth and legend, and revels in what it finds there; hence we witness in Moore's reclining women not the female nude in her modernist pose as a chilled object of form, but in a far more ancient role, that of a warmly beneficent eternal earth goddess, a primal female being who proudly displays her abundant fertility in the fullness of her forms. It may seem surprising to discover this Mediterranean character in a native of the isles which the ancient Romans situated at the furthest northern boundary of their known world. Moore was neither a doctrinaire nor a sentimental classicist, however. He admired the roughness of archaic Greek sculpture, but not the realistic representation of the later Greeks, which, he lamented, came to prevail in European sculpture during the Renaissance and down through modern times. Moore wrote:

"The removal of the Greek spectacles from the eyes of the sculptor (along with the direction given by the work of such painters as Cézanne and Seurat) has helped him to realise again the intrinsic emotional significance of shapes instead of seeing mainly a representation value, and freed him to recognise again the importance of the material in which he works... A limitless scope is open to him. His inspiration will come, as always, from nature and the world around him, from which he learns such principles as balance, rhythm, organic growth of life, attraction and repulsion, harmony and contrast... Each sculptor differs in his aims and ideals according to his different character, personality and his point of development. The sculpture which moves me most is full blooded and self-supporting, fully in the round, that is, its components are completely realised and work as masses in opposition... it is not perfectly symmetrical, it is static and it is strong and vital, giving out something of the energy and power of great mountains. It has a life of its own, independent of the object it represents."

1 HENRY MOORE (1898-1986)

Family Group

bronze with brown and green patina
Height: 6 in. (15.3 cm.)
Conceived in 1944 and cast in the artist's lifetime

$500,000-700,000

PROVENANCE:
Fischer Fine Art, London.
Weintraub Gallery, New York.
Acquired from the above by the present owner, 1995.

LITERATURE:
H. Read, *Henry Moore: Sculpture and Drawings*, New York, 1949, no. 70h (terracotta version illustrated).
D. Sylvester, ed., *Henry Moore: Complete Sculpture 1921-48*, London, 1988, vol. 1, p. 14, no. 230 (terracotta version illustrated, p. 144). J. Hedgecoe and H. Moore, *Henry Moore*, New York, 1968, p. 176, no. 1 (another cast illustrated).

(fig. 1) Henry Moore, *Family Group*, 1944 (terra cotta sketch-model for the present bronze version). Henry Moore Foundation, Much Hadham.

Reproduced by permission of the Henry Moore Foundation

It has been customary to attribute Moore's interest in doing Family Groups to the event in 1946 when his wife Irina gave birth of his daughter Mary, their only child. Mary was a miraculous arrival; the sculptor was forty-seven, and his wife was thirty-nine; her previous pregnancies had ended in miscarriages. In the context of Moore's art, however, Mary's birth was actually more of a timely coincidence—the sculptor had already been actively treating this theme for two years previously, while engaged in a project for a public family sculpture that dated back to before the Second World War. Moore later recalled:

"When Walter Gropius was working in England before the war he was asked by Henry Morris, Director for Education in Cambridgeshire to design a large school at Impington, near Cambridge. It was called a Village College and was meant to be different from other elementary schools because it was meant to put into practice lots of Henry Morris' ideas on education. Gropius asked me to do a piece of sculpture for the school. We talked about it and I suggested that a family group would be the right subject Later the war came and I heard no more about until, about 1944, Henry Morris told me that he now thought he could get enough money together for the sculpture if I would still like to think of doing it. I said yes, because the idea right from the start had appealed to me and I began drawings in note book form of family groups. From these notebook drawings I made a number of small maquettes, a dozen or more. Some of the maquettes were ideas for bronze (fig. 1; terracotta sketch-model for the present sculpture), but most of them were for stone because for the Impington school I felt stone would be the suitable material" (quoted in A. Wilkinson, ed., *Henry Moore: Writings and Conversations*, Berkeley, 2002, p. 273).

10 HENRY MOORE (1898-1986)

Reclining Woman: Elbow

signed and numbered 'Moore 1/9' (on the top of the base);
inscribed with foundry mark 'Morris Singer FOUNDERS LONDON'
(on the back of the base)
bronze with brown patina
Length: 94⅜ in. (239.8 cm.)
Conceived and cast in 1981

$3,500,000-4,500,000

PROVENANCE:

Anon. sale, Sotheby's, New York, 8 November 1994,
lot 44.
Jeffrey H. Loria & Co., Inc., New York.
Acquired from the above by the present owner,
5 October 1995.

LITERATURE:

R. Berthoud, *The Life of Henry Moore*, New York,
1987, no. 174 (another cast illustrated).
A. Bowness, ed., *Henry Moore: Complete Sculpture
1980-86*, London, 1988, vol. 6, p. 38, no. 810
(another cast illustrated, p. 41; another cast
illustrated again, pls 59-62).

Reclining Woman: Elbow is one of Moore's final monumental sculptures, created when the artist was eighty-three years old. Roger Berthoud, the sculptor's biographer, declared, "the imposingly sensual *Reclining Woman: Elbow*" was "arguably Moore's last significant new sculpture" (in *The Life of Henry Moore*, New York, 1987, p. 402). The superlative beauty and power that Moore invested in this valedictory Reclining Woman sums up six decades of the sculptor's unflagging capacity for thematic variation and formal invention, and stands as an ultimate monument to his consummate mastery of a subject which had engrossed him throughout his career. Moore wrote, "From the very beginning the reclining figure has been my main theme. The first one I made was around 1924, and probably more than half of my sculptures since have been reclining figures" (quoted in J. Hedgecoe, *Henry Moore*, New York, 1968, p. 151).

"The human figure is the basis of all my sculpture," Moore stated, "and that for me means the female nude." He enumerated the three basic poses of the human figure: standing, sitting and lying down. In the vast majority of his works the female figure is seen sitting or reclining, a preference that initially stemmed from his desire to work in stone, for the practical concern that a standing figure in carved stone is structurally weak at the ankles. "But with either a seated or reclining figure one doesn't have this worry. And between them are enough variations to occupy any sculptor for a lifetime." He noted, moreover, that "of the three poses the reclining figure gives the most freedom, compositionally and spatially. The seated figure has to have something to sit on. You can't free it from its pedestal. A reclining figure can recline on any surface. It is free and stable at the same time. It fits in with my belief

(fig. 1)

(fig. 2)

David Sylvester observed that most of Moore's reclining women were nudes, "but, though they lie with knees apart or thighs apart, their overall pose doesn't betoken the availability commonly implied in reclining female nudes" (in *Henry Moore*, exh. cat., Tate Gallery, London, 1968, p. 5). Since the time of Ingres, Delacroix and Renoir, the tradition of the reclining female figure in European painting has been inextricably tied to the Orientalist convention of the odalisque, the nude or partly clad but always voluptuous harem girl, playing her part in a deliberately titillating show of veiled or blatant eroticism. Moore's conception of the reclining woman, even when nude, runs counter to this tradition. Moore stated, "I am not conscious of erotic elements in [my work], and I have never set out to create an erotic work of art... I have no objection to people interpreting my forms and sculptures erotically... but I do not have any desire to rationalise the eroticism in my work, to think out consciously what Freudian or Jungian symbols may lie behind what I create" (quoted in A. Wilkinson, ed., *Henry Moore: Writings and Conversations*, Berkeley, 2002, p. 115).

This disavowal of erotic intent, a rare admission in an important modern artist, was not the consequence of any latter-day Puritannical streak in Moore's make-up. Rather, it seems, he was disinclined to reduce human sexuality—and more specifically, the especially sensitive issues concerning female sexuality—to prurient fetishistic content, which would only serve to demean his subjects. Albert Elsen noted that Moore "always honors and never humiliates his feminine subjects. They are sensual but not flagrantly or even coyly erotic" (in *Modern European Sculpture 1918-1945*, New York, 1978, p. 50). No other great artist of the 20th century was as sympathetic as Moore to the complex and multi-dimensional lives of women and respectful of their all-important role in human society. Surely none other expressed—so powerfully, convincingly and sensitively—his awe and veneration of their miraculous life-giving and nurturing powers. The Reclining Women were Moore's powerful monument to Woman as all women. Moore favored the "Rounded forms [that] convey an idea of fruitfulness," and in this light Will Grohmann called attention to the fact that his women express a universal significance:

"These reclining women are not the reclining women of a Maillol [see lot 67] or a Matisse: they are women in repose but also something more profound the woman as the concept of fruitfulness, the Mother Earth. Moore, who once pointed to the maternal element in the 'Reclining Figures', may well see in them an element of eternity, the 'Great Female', who is both birth-giving nature and the wellspring of the unconscious. To Henry Moore, the 'Reclining Figures' are no mere external objects, he identifies himself with them, as well as the earth and the whole realm of motherhood (in *The Art of Henry Moore*, London, 1960, p. 43).

(fig. 1) Michelangelo Buonarrati, *La Notte*, 1520-1534. Tomba dei Giuliano dei Medici, Capelle dei Medici, Florence.
(fig. 2) Chacmool figure, Mayan-Toltec limestone carving, *circa* 900-1,000AD. Museo Nacional de Antropología, Mexico City.

(fig. 3) (fig. 4)

(fig. 3) Henry Moore, *Reclining Figure*, 1929. Leeds City Art Gallery and Temple Newsam House. (fig. 4) Henry Moore, *UNESCO Reclining Figure*, 1957-1958. UNESCO Headquarters, Paris.

Even in repose, the horizontal format of the reclining women fosters the illusion that plastic energy is being transmitted from one end to the other along the length of the form, and in giving shape to this internal power Moore has transformed the figure and created an equivalency with the larger natural landscape. David Sylvester believed that an archaic and deeply-embedded vein of mythical inspiration manifest itself in Moore's reclining figures. He wrote, "Personifications such as river-gods of nature's flowing energy are traditional pretexts for sculptures of reclining figures. Moore's figures, of course, represent nothing but themselves, but are made to look as if they themselves had been shaped by nature's energy. They seem to be weathered, eroded, tunnelled-into by the action of wind and water Moore's reclining figures are not supine; they prop themselves up, are potentially active. Hence the affinity with river-gods: the idea is not simply that of a body subjected to the flow of nature's forces but of one in which those forces are harnessed" (in *Henry Moore*, exh. cat., Tate Gallery, London, 1968, p. 5).

The great precedents for the reclining female nude in European sculpture are Michelangelo's figures representing *Day* and *Night* (fig. 1) that adorn the Medici chapel in Florence, works which also strongly influenced both Maillol and Matisse. The most direct sources, however, for Moore's vision of the female figure were the sculptures of ancient and primitive cultures, from the Paleolithic period, Sumer, Assyria, Egypt, archaic Greece and Italy, as well as African tribal art (see note to lot 12). In contrast to the brooding drama in Michelangelo's Renaissance figures, the reclining form in these ancient arts usually represents the figure in repose, engaged in quiescent contemplation of the world, the heavens, and human destiny. Moore was especially drawn to the stone carvings of the Toltec, Mayan and Aztec societies of Pre-Columbian Central America. He especially admired Mexican carving for its "vigorous simplicity, power, almost fierceness... Mexican stone sculptures have largeness of scale & a grim, sublime austerity, a real stoniness. They were true sculptures in sympathy with their material & their sculpture has some of the character of mountains, of boulders, rocks and sea worn pebbles" (unpublished notes, 1925-1926, in A. Wilkinson, ed., *op. cit.*, p. 97).

The key work of Mexican sculpture for Moore was the reclining Chacmool, the Toltec-Mayan Rain Spirit discovered in Chichén-Nítza (fig. 2). The artist's own recollection of where and when he first encountered this revelatory sculpture differs from other evidence; in any case it appears that he saw a plaster cast of the original stone carving in Paris at the Trocadéro (now the Musée de l'Homme) in 1922, and he came across the Chacmool once again a few years later in Berlin when he saw the work illustrated in a German book on Mexican art. "It was the pose that struck me—this idea of a figure being on its back and turned upwards to the sky instead of lying on it side... Its stillness and alertness, a sense of readiness—and the whole presence of it, and the legs coming down like columns" (quoted in *ibid.*, p. 98). Moore's appreciation of the Chacmool had the effect of liberating him from a sense of obligation to depicting the figure in any realistic or conventional manner. The Chacmool's strange conjunction of head, torso and limbs inspired the sculptor to create seemingly unlimited and expressively pointed variations on the body in a recumbent pose. The influence of the Chacmool is readily apparent in the so-called Leeds *Reclining Figure*, 1929 (Lund Humphries, no. 59; fig. 3), and may be seen to resonate, in varying ways, in almost every reclining woman that Moore made thereafter, including, in this catalogue, *Two Piece Reclining Figure: Armless* (lot 18) and the present *Reclining Woman: Elbow*.

Sylvester has noted "Moore's avowed and manifest insistence on asymmetry," a guiding principle which stemmed from the sculptor's interest in the Chacmool. "A reclining figure is asymmetrical from every angle," Sylvester explained. "In insuring that it is, Moore creates an opposition between the two halves which tends to undermine their continuity" (*op. cit.*, p. 6). The female theme may have been Moore's essential inspiration, but the engine which drove his work from day to day was his seemingly inexhaustible capacity for plastic invention and variation. The tensions and oppositions inherent in the asymmetrical reclining figure were ideally suited to this approach. Moore declared:

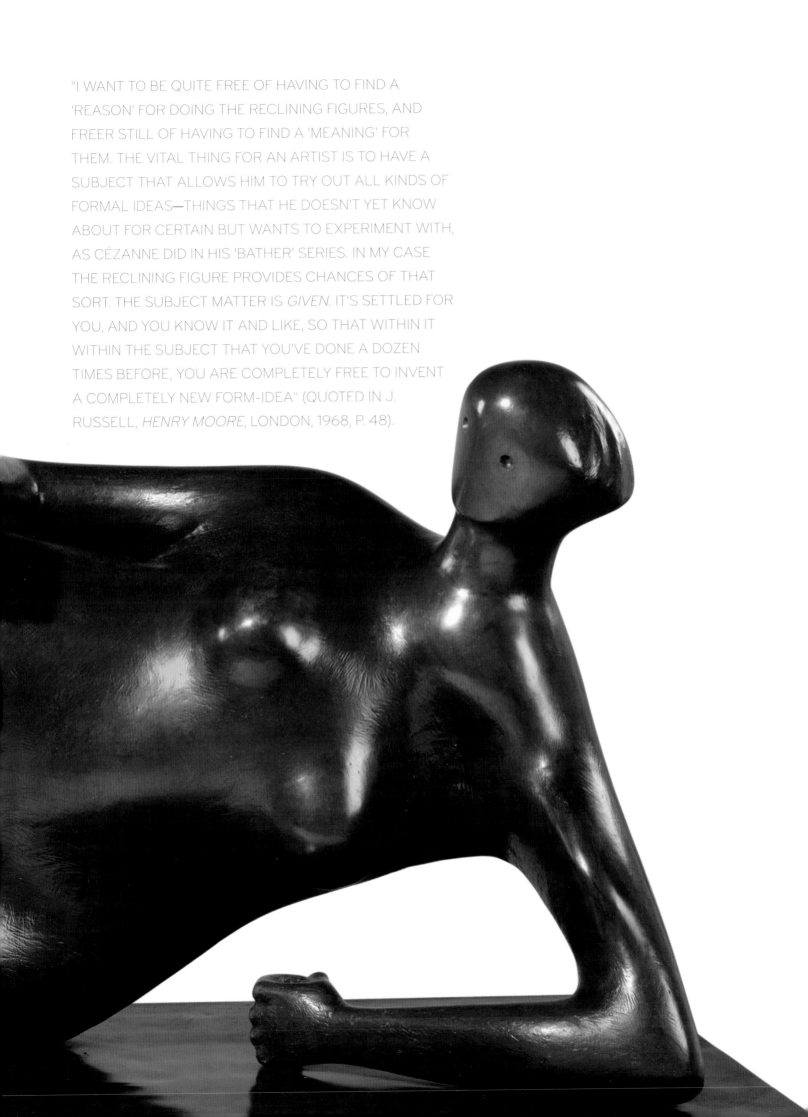

"I WANT TO BE QUITE FREE OF HAVING TO FIND A 'REASON' FOR DOING THE RECLINING FIGURES, AND FREER STILL OF HAVING TO FIND A 'MEANING' FOR THEM. THE VITAL THING FOR AN ARTIST IS TO HAVE A SUBJECT THAT ALLOWS HIM TO TRY OUT ALL KINDS OF FORMAL IDEAS—THINGS THAT HE DOESN'T YET KNOW ABOUT FOR CERTAIN BUT WANTS TO EXPERIMENT WITH, AS CÉZANNE DID IN HIS 'BATHER' SERIES. IN MY CASE THE RECLINING FIGURE PROVIDES CHANCES OF THAT SORT. THE SUBJECT MATTER IS *GIVEN*. IT'S SETTLED FOR YOU, AND YOU KNOW IT AND LIKE, SO THAT WITHIN IT WITHIN THE SUBJECT THAT YOU'VE DONE A DOZEN TIMES BEFORE, YOU ARE COMPLETELY FREE TO INVENT A COMPLETELY NEW FORM-IDEA" (QUOTED IN J. RUSSELL, *HENRY MOORE*, LONDON, 1968, P. 48).

(fig. 5)

(fig. 5) Edgar Degas, *Paysage*, *circa* 1890-1892. Private collection.

Moore's pre-war reclining figures display a balance of formal elements that manifest, in Elsen's words, "a quiet majesty, an aloofness and serenity" (*ibid.*). The experience of the Second World War, and the profoundly felt shelter drawings he made during the London Blitz, led Moore to introduce a more anxious and unsettled attitude into his post-war sculpture, especially in those works in which he divided the reclining figure in pieces (see lot 18). Here, however, nearing the end of this magnificent line of recumbent women, Moore returned to a more classically whole and integrated expression of the female form, as seen in the earlier *UNESCO Reclining Figure*, 1957-1958 (Lund Humphries, no. 416; fig. 4). This late reclining woman, however, is less abstract, and while she is still impressively domineering in her massiveness, her sensual appeal is warmly inviting. This woman has taken on her ancient role as a beneficent and life-affirming fertility goddess—she is the very earth itself. In Cézanne's great bather paintings the nude and landscape enter into a synergistic pictorial bond, and in a late Degas pastel the form of a reclining woman may be detected in the topography of a coastal landscape (fig. 5). For Moore, woman is landscape, landscape is woman, and the reclining figure evokes the rolling hills, fields and vales of the sculptor's adopted home of Hertfordshire. Wilkinson stated, "One of Moore's greatest contributions to the language of twentieth century sculpture has been the use of the human figure as metaphor for landscape" (in "Henry Moore's Reclining Women," *National Gallery of Canada Annual Bulletin*, vol. 1, 1977-1978).

There are three openings in the form of this reclining woman, one contained within the shape of her arm, bent at the elbow, on which she leans and amazingly appears to support her massive weight; another is the space between the lower legs at the foot of the sculpture. And there is, of course, the large hole that separates her thighs, to which the viewer's eye is instantly and deliberately drawn. The hole is a signature element carried forward from some of Moore's earliest works (see lot 14). Here the hole connotes negative space—or as Moore put it, "a shape which could have turned into a solid form if I had thought of it the other way around"—and, taking the artist's permission to interpret these forms as we are so inclined, it may serves as a visual metaphor for a sexual orifice, the opening of the birth-canal, or the womb; or in terms of the landscape, it is a cave opening, the shape of a pond, or merely the amplified shape of a smooth pebble. Moore wrote in 1937, "There's no doubt a deep psychological explanation for the fascination of the hole" (quoted in A. Wilkinson, ed., *op. cit.*, 2002, p. 207).

Of all Moore's subjects, only the Reclining Woman could bear the weight of these many inferences, and sustain the profound and far-reaching metaphor by which our bodies, as the sculptor tells us, become the world. While other themes came, went and returned in Moore's work, Russell rightly asserted that "the obsession with the Reclining Figure has stayed with Moore forever" (*op. cit.*, p. 48). Moore wrote:

"Our own bodies, our own make up, have the greatest influence on art... For me everything in the world of form is understood through our own bodies. From our mother's breast, from our bones, from bumping into things, we learn what is rough and what is smooth. To observe, to understand, to experience the vast variety of space, shape and form in the world, twenty lifetimes would not be enough. There is no end to it" (quoted in *ibid.*, pp. 220 and 221).

12 HENRY MOORE (1898-1986)
Figure

boxwood
Height: 17 in. (43.2 cm.)
Executed in 1932; unique

$600,000-800,000

PROVENANCE:
Collection of the artist (until at least 1949).
Harold Diamond, New York (by 1957).
M. Knoedler & Co., Inc., New York.
Louis Honig, San Francisco (acquired from the above 28 February 1968). By descent from the above to the present owner, 1983.

LITERATURE:
H. Read, *Henry Moore: Sculpture and Drawings*, New York, 1949, no. 78a (illustrated).
R. Melville, *Henry Moore: Sculpture and Drawings 1921-1969*, London, 1970, no. 62 (illustrated).
D. Mitchinson, ed., *Henry Moore Sculpture*, London, 1981, p. 56, no. 76 (illustrated).
D. Sylvester, ed., *Henry Moore: Complete Sculpture 1921-48*, London, 1988, vol. 1, p. 8, no. 113 (illustrated, p. 10).

(fig. 1) Mumuye funerary ancestor figure, Northern Nigeria. The British Museum, London.

"Yesterday I spent my second afternoon in the British Museum with the Egyptian and Assyrian sculptures," Moore wrote to his friend, Jocelyn Horner, on October 29, 1921. "An hour before closing time I tore myself away from these to do a little exploring and found—in the Ethnographical Gallery—the ecstatically fine negro sculptures" (in A. Wilkinson, ed., *Henry Moore: Writings and Conversations*, Los Angeles, 2002, p. 45). Moore paid weekly visits to the British Museum during his university years in London, drawn particularly by "the world tradition—the big view of Sculpture" that he discovered in its collections of primitive art, from Palaeolithic fertility goddesses, Cycladic and early Greek art to African, Oceanic, and Pre-Columbian sculpture (quoted in A. Wilkinson, "Henry Moore's Reclining Woman," *Annual Bulletin* 1, National Gallery of Canada, 1977-78). Moore particularly admired the "wonderfully fertile invention of abstract forms" in tribal carving (in A. Wilkinson, *op. cit.*, 2002, p. 98). The opened-out three-dimensionality of those figures became an important point of departure for his own sculpture as it developed into the 1930s.

Moore produced some of his most abstract carvings during this time, experimenting with sculpture in the round and multiform configurations of space carved out of solid form. His emphasis on a fully three-dimensional treatment of form and on the principle of "truth to material"—the bedrock of his philosophy of art—followed from his study of African sculpture. He credited African wood carvings with helping him to "realize the intrinsic emotional significance of shapes as distinct from their representational values" and to "recognise the importance of the material in which he worked" (in *ibid.*, p. 99). These sculptural values elegantly define the organic contours of *Figure*: the vertical graining of the wood parallels the outline of the feminized body, and the openings between the torso and limbs suggest the plasticity and spatial presence of fully realized three-dimensional form.

The present sculpture may allude to a Mumuye funerary ancestor figure (fig. 1) at the British Museum, which Moore declared "one of the best from this point of view. The carver has managed to make it 'spatial' by the way in which he has made the arms free and yet enveloping the central form of the body" (quoted in *ibid.*, p. 107). Here, as in *Figure*, it was possible to create openings within the body of the form without giving the appearance and even the actuality of structural weakness, which was a special concern when Moore worked in stone. The cylindrical form and upward growth expressed in both carvings honor the natural properties of wood, and they exemplify the sympathetic respect that the artist held for the individual character, or truth, of his material. The vertical energy of this *Figure*, captured in the subtly upturned angle of its dished face, is balanced by the grounded stability of the truncated legs, rooted in the earth. In its organic vitality, it embodies Moore's appreciation for the "serious and pathetic power—a bigness and monumental simplicity" of the African tradition (quoted in *ibid.*, p. 99).

14 HENRY MOORE (1898-1986)

Figure

travertine marble
Height: 16¾ in. (39.9 cm.)
Executed in 1933-1934; unique

$1,800,000-2,500,000

PROVENANCE:
Buchholz Gallery, New York.
H. Cady Wells, Santa Fe (by 1949).
Private collection, Switzerland.
Acquired from the above by the present owner,
1990.

EXHIBITED:
New York, The Museum of Modern Art, 1946, p. 29,
no. 25 (illustrated).
Paris, Didier Imbert Fine Arts, *Henry Moore Intime*,
April-July 1992, p. 159 (illustrated).
Tokyo, Sezon Museum of Art, *Henry Moore Intime*,
September-November 1992.

LITERATURE:
H. Read, *Henry Moore: Sculpture and Drawings*,
New York, 1949 (illustrated, pl. 34b).
W. Grohmann, *The Art of Henry Moore*, London,
1960, p. 105 (illustrated, pl. 84).
J. Hedgecoe, ed., *Henry Moore*, New York, 1968, p.
86, no. 5 (illustrtaed).
J. Russell, *Henry Moore*, New York, 1968, p. 50, no.
47 (illustrated).
R. Melville, *Henry Moore: Sculpture and Drawings
1921-1969*, London, 1970, no. 90 (illustrated).
D. Mitchinson, ed., *Henry Moore: Sculpture*,
London, 1981,p. 58, no. 80 (illustrated).
D. Sylvester, ed., *Henry Moore: Sculpture 1921-
1948*, London, 1988, vol. 1, p. 8, no. 137
(illustrated, p. 11).
A. Wilkinson, ed., *Henry Moore: Writings and
Conversations*, Los Angeles, 2002, p. 206
(illustrated; illustrated again in color on the cover).

"All art is an abstraction to some degree," Moore reflected in 1934, in a statement written for Unit One, an avant-garde group at the forefront of the British modern movement, which he had joined the previous year. "Abstract qualities of design are essential to the value of a work, but to me of equal importance is the psychological human element. If both abstract and human elements are welded together in a work, it must have a fuller, deeper meaning" (quoted in A. Wilkinson, ed., *Henry Moore: Writings and Conversations*, Berkeley, 2002, p. 133). As Moore's sculpture evolved in the 1930s, the pull of pure plastic invention drew him toward the language of abstraction, and the human dimension of his work began to take on radical new forms. The tendency toward abstraction dovetailed with a growing attraction to the Surrealist mythology of the unconscious mind, and Moore drew productively from both developments as he sought, in his words, to "charge an 'abstract' shape with meaning—to impregnate form with vitality—to give an organic life to non-realistic, non-representational sculpture—to make a shape strangely significant, without knowing how, or why it is so" (quoted in *ibid.*, p. 199).

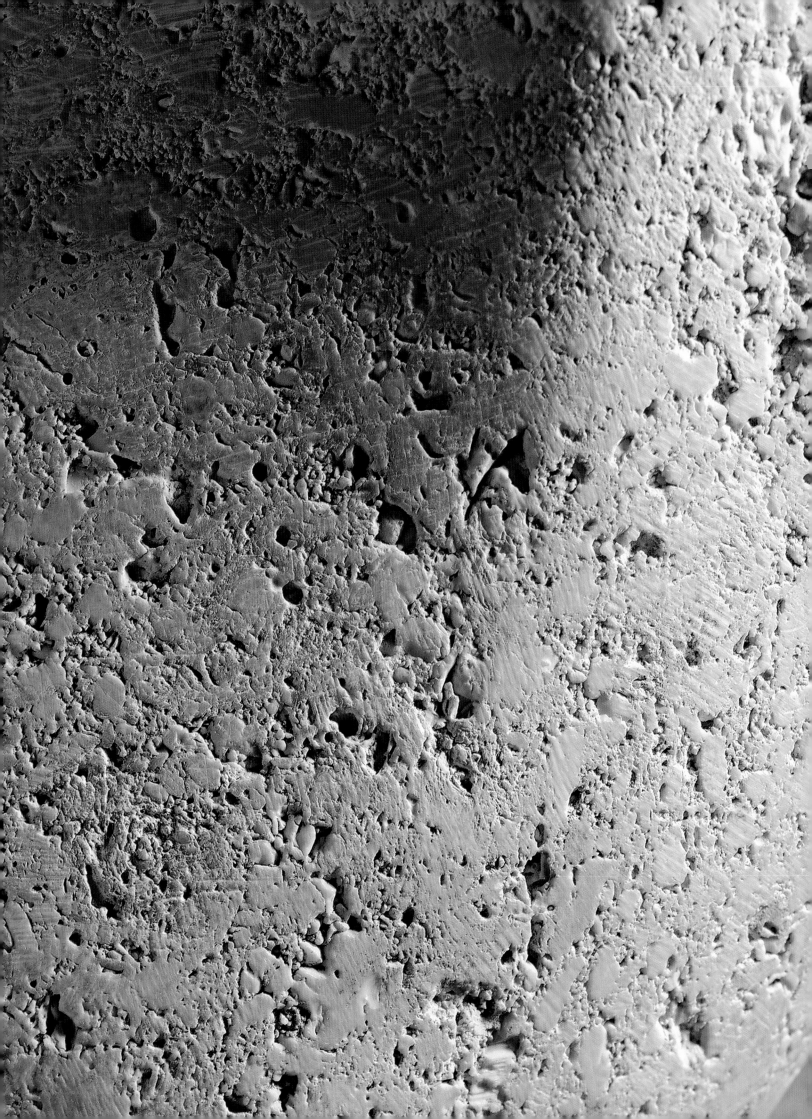

(fig. 1)

The sculptural problem of how to realize an integral mass in three-dimensional space had preoccupied Moore throughout the 1920s. Having shaken off the limitations of relief by the end of the decade, Moore began to hollow out forms, taking a cue from the open volumes of Picasso's sculptures (fig. 1), which suggested new ways of incorporating empty, negative space within a composition. He eventually opened up the stone entirely with the new, dynamic element of the hole. "The first hole made through a piece of stone is a revelation," he marveled in 1937. "The hole connects one side to the other, making it immediately more three-dimensional. A hole can itself have as much shape-meaning as a solid mass. Sculpture in air is possible, where the stone contains only the hole, which is the intended and considered form" (quoted in *ibid.*, pp. 195-96). In the present Figure, the central hole asserts its shape fully in its own right, penetrating the stone and creating an integral plastic rhythm that spreads centrifugally through the entire block of marble. The dynamism of the hole, carried over into the figure's dramatically slanting shoulders, breathes vital energy into the travertine, linking each side to the other and making visible the depth of its form. "One of the things I would like to think my sculpture has is a force, is a strength, is a life, a vitality from inside it," Moore once remarked, "so that you have a sense that the form is pressing from inside trying to burst or trying to give off the strength from inside itself, rather than having something which is just shaped from outside and stopped. It's as though you have something trying to make itself come to a shape from inside itself" (quoted in *ibid.*, p. 198).

A central tenet of Moore's approach to sculpture in the 1930s was his belief in the doctrine of "truth to material." Following Brancusi, Moore believed that "when the sculptor works direct, when there is an active relationship with his material, that the material can take its part in the shaping of an idea. Stone, for example, is hard and concentrated and should keep its hard tense stoniness" (quoted in *ibid.*, p. 191). Moore praised travertine in particular as "ruddy, powerful, strong. You feel you haven't got to handle it with kid gloves" (quoted in *ibid.*, p. 223). *Figure* presents an early limit case for Moore's dictum that "a piece of stone can have a hole through it and not be weakened": by carving directly through the block, he demonstrates the plastic resilience and dynamic vitality of the stone, which "on the principle of the archcan remain just as strong" (quoted in *ibid.*, p. 195).

Moore's engagement with abstraction gave new visibility to the properties of his material, but he was always careful to emphasize the underlying organicism of his carvings and their essential humanity. "There's no doubt a deep psychological explanation of the fascination of the hole," Moore admitted, and *Figure's* curves and central cavity do intimate a corporeal presence that allusively suggests the recesses and undulations of the female form (quoted in *ibid.*, p. 207). For Moore the human presence was both innate and subjective, alive within the material itself and shaped by the history of human experience. "As the piece of stone or wood I carve evolves from the first roughening-out stages it begins to take on a definite human personality and character," he observed. "A more active relationship gets going, which calls upon the same sort of feelings one has about people in real life. And to bring the work to its final conclusion involves one's whole psychological make-up and whatever one can draw upon and make use of from the sum total of one's human and form experience" (quoted in *ibid.*, p. 126).

(fig. 1) Pablo Picasso, *Metamorphosis I*, 1928. Musée Picasso, Paris.

18 HENRY MOORE (1898-1986)

Two Piece Reclining Figure: Armless

black granite
(Body) Height: 55¼ in. (140.3 cm.) (Legs) Length: 58½ in. (148.6 cm.)
Executed in 1977; unique

$3,500,000-4,500,000

PROVENANCE:

Family of the artist (by descent from artist).
Jeffrey H. Loria & Co., Inc., New York (acquired from the above).
Acquired from the above by the present owner, 2 September 2002.

EXHIBITED:

London, Serpentine Gallery and Kensington Gardens, *Henry Moore at the Serpentine: 80th Birthday Exhibition of recent carvings and bronzes*, July-October 1978.

LITERATURE:

G. Levine, *With Henry Moore: The Artist at Work*, London, 1978, p. 141 (illustrated, pp. 142-143).
A. Bowness, ed., *Henry Moore, Complete Sculpture 1974-1980*, London, 1983, vol. 5, no. 686 (illustrated; illustrated again pls. 64-67).

Reproduced by permission of the Henry Moore Foundation

(fig. 1) Henry Moore, *Two-Piece Reclining Figure No. 1*, 1959; Chelsea School of Art, London Institute.

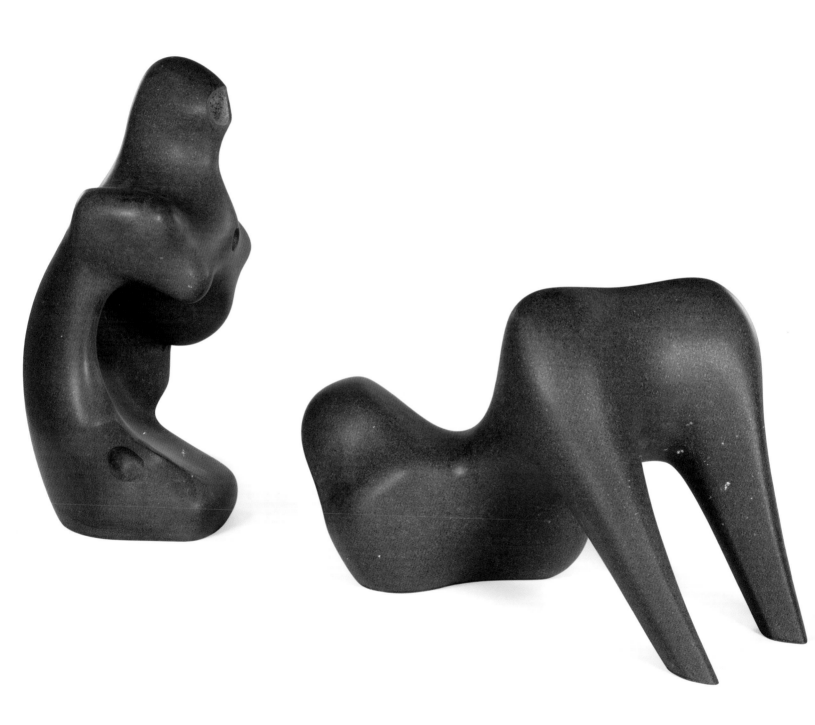

Moore carved this *Two Piece Reclining Figure: Armless* from black granite, a material which, unlike the reflective surface of bronze, absorbs and diffuses the light that is cast on it, softening its forms, and lending it a darkly sensual aspect that seems to belie the very hardness of the material from which it is made. The sculptor once wrote, "In stone sculpture you have to alter the malleable softness of flesh and blood into something that is harder and less bendable" (quoted in A. Wilkinson, ed., *Henry Moore:Writings and Conversations*, Berkeley, 2002, p. 222). Here it may be said that Moore has performed this act of transubstantiation in reverse, having turned something that is hard and unbendable into a body that almost seems soft and malleable.

Carved in 1977, this nude woman comes near the end of a long line of reclining figures, the quintessential subject in Moore's oeuvre from the very outset of his career (see note to lot 10). The most dramatic aspect of this figure is, of course, that it has been cut into two pieces. Although Moore created multi-piece compositions in modest table-top dimensions during the 1930s, he did not divide the reclining female form in a large scale sculpture until 1959, when he made *Two- Piece Reclining Figure No. 1* (Lund Humphries, no. 457; fig. 1), measuring 76 inches (193 cm.). This significant development suggested further possibilities—Moore subsequently created numerous other two-piece figures, and during the 1960s and 1970s, three-piece and four-piece works as well (Lund Humphries, no. 629; fig. 2).

By constricting the waist of *Reclining Figure*, 1934 (Lund Humphries, no. 141; fig. 3), so that the horizontal body becomes bulging forms at either end, Moore suggested that he might ultimately break the figure into two parts, and that each element would have a pronounced vertical emphasis. Moore did in fact create a series of multi-piece sculptures that year, including *Four-Piece Composition: Reclining Figure* (Lund Humphries, no. 154). Commentators have noted the surrealist influence on these works; Steven A. Nash has pointed out that "The idea of spreading a sculptural composition across a flat base, so antithetical to the ancient tradition of the vertical statue, was very much in the air at the time. Moore would have seen examples in work by Arp, and certainly was aware of Giacometti's repeated and highly inventive use of the device" (in *Henry Moore: Sculpting the 20th Century*, exh. cat., Dallas Museum of Art, 2001, pp. 46-47). The act of cutting the figure into sections might initially appear as a perversely wanton act of surrealist violence. However, in contrast to the transgressive psycho-sexual attitudes that normally informed surrealist imagery, especially as seen in Giacometti's sculptures of this period, Moore's composite figures "are serene, psychologically neutral studies in formal balance and rhythmic variation" (*ibid.*, p. 47).

Moore carried these abstract formal values, as well their essentially serene aspect, over into his later reclining figures. He viewed the sectioned figure in terms of his evolving conception of the human form as part of a larger natural order, and he conceived his large post-war multi-piece sculptures as existing in a symbiotic harmony with the open-air landscape. The sculptor wrote that *Two Piece Reclining Figure No. 1*, 1959, "is a mixture of rock form and mountains combined with the human figure I don't think it was a conscious or intentional thing for me to break up the figures in this way, but I suppose those earlier works, from the thirties had something to do with it... I did the first one in pieces almost without intending to. But after I had done it, then the second one became a conscious idea. I realized what an advantage a separated two-piece composition could have in relating figures to landscape. Knees and breasts are mountains. Once these two parts become separated, you don't expect a naturalistic figure; therefore you can justifiably make it like a landscape or rock" (quoted in A.Wilkinson, ed., *op. cit.*, pp. 287-288).

(fig. 2)

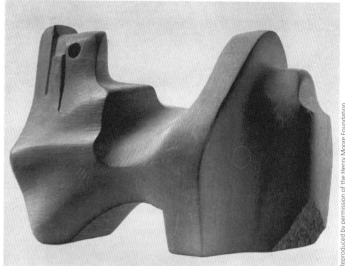
(fig. 3)

Reproduced by permission of the Henry Moore Foundation

The figure and landscape contained corresponding formal elements, and, as metaphor, one could be understood in the terms of the other. Moore explained, "All experience of space and world starts from physical sensation. This also explains the deformation of my figures. They are not at all distortions of the body's shape. I think, rather, that in the image of the human body one can also express something nonhuman— landscape, for instance—in exactly the same way as we live over again mountains and valleys in our bodily sensations. Or think of the basic poetic element in metaphor: there too we express one thing in the image of another. It seems to me that I can say more about the world as a whole by means of such poetic interpenetrations than I could with the human figure alone"(quoted in S. Compton, *Henry Moore*, exh. cat., Royal Academy of Arts, 1988, p. 259).

The body forms in Moore's multi-part reclining figures shapes were occasionally influenced by other landscape references from the art of earlier masters. Moore wrote, "the leg end [of *Two Piece Reclining Form No. 1*] began to remind me as I was working on it of Seurat's *Le Bec du Hoc* (fig. 4), which Kenneth Clark owned. I had seen it on numerous occasions and have always admired it" (in D. Mitchinson, ed., *op. cit.*, p. 153). He likewise described the arching leg end of *Two Piece Reclining Figure No. 2*, 1960 (Lund Humphries, no. 458) in terms of the cliff forms in Monet's *Le Manneporte (Étretat)* (The Metropolitan Museum of Art, New York). Indeed, both allusions are pertinent to the present sculpture as well: the armless torso recalls the rocky thrust of Seurat's *Le Bec du Hoc*, and the each of the legs bent at the knee bring to mind the dramatic natural arch form at Etretat, as seen in Monet's paintings. Moore stated, "Sculpture is a mixture of the human figure and landscape, a metaphor of the relationship of humanity with the earth" (quoted in A. Wilkinson, ed., *op. cit.*, p. 289).

In addition to drawing attention to the relationships between the body and landscape, Moore took advantage of the multi-part composition to create a more enhanced and varied viewing experience. He explained, "Dividing the figure into two parts made many more three-dimensional variations than if it had just been a monolithic piece," he wrote. "If it is two pieces, there's a bigger surprise, you have more unexpected views. The front view doesn't enable one to foresee the back view. As you move around it, the two parts overlap or they open up and there's space between" (quoted in D. Mitchinson, ed., *op. cit.*, p. 157). The simple logic of this revelation inspired Moore to create sculptures of increasing complexity, both in their totality and in their parts. "I obtain many permutations and combinations. By adding two pieces together the differences are not simply doubled. As in mathematics, they are geometrically multiplied, producing an infinite variety of viewpoints" (quoted in J. Hedgecoe, *Henry Moore*, New York, 1968, p. 504).

(fig. 2) Henry Moore, *Large Four Piece Reclining Figure*, 1972-1973. Sold, Christie's New York, 2 May 2006, lot 31.
(fig. 3) Henry Moore, *Reclining Figure*, 1934. Private collection.

John Russell understood Moore's two-piece idea as a means of opening up "possibilities of tension and antithesis, statement and counter-statement, which simply could not be explored in a single form" (in *Henry Moore*, London, 1973, p. 211). Moore invited the viewer to move actively around his sectioned figures, and to look *into* them, to contemplate the subtle relationships between mass and space, the positioning of volumes, the contrasts between surface contours, and the juxtaposition of external and internal aspects. "Sculpture is a like a journey," Moore remarked. "You have a different view as you return" (quoted in D. Mitchinson, ed., *op. cit.*, p. 157). Moore's manipulation of space between the sections is no less calculated than the forms of the bronze components themselves. Moore wrote, "This space is terribly important and is as much a form as the actual solid, and should be looked upon as a piece of form or a shape just as much as the actual material" (in *ibid.*, 266).

Moore's choice of carved black granite as the material for *Two-Piece Reclining Figure: Armless* is absolutely essential to his idea of conception of this work; it was fortunate that as he neared his eightieth year he still possessed the stamina to work in stone, the material he had preferred in his earliest sculptures. He declared, "In those days I loved stone, as I still do now. I actually love stone. A piece of stone, any piece of stone in a landscape, a big rock, anything in stone, I just love more even than I love wood" (quoted in A. Wilkinson, ed., *op. cit.*, p. 222). Moore pointed out that "Granite is one of the hardest stones, it would last for thousands of years in any climate. Very few other stones will stay out of doors as well as bronze" (quoted in *ibid.*). Indeed, rock embodies the very essence of the two-piece idea, as John Russell has noted:

"In the two-piece Reclining Figures Moore can afford to let our attention wander at will: what does not come in with one tide will come in with the next. The tidal image is not chosen at random. If these pieces have any one single secondary signficance, it is that of an eroded coast... If Walter Pater were to come back to earth and see one of these figures he would not say of it, as he said of the *Mona Lisa*, that she was 'older than the rocks among which she sits': he would say that she *was* those rocks. Rock and woman are one in these pieces..." (*op. cit.*, pp. 202 and 205).

(fig. 4) Georges Seurat, *Le Bec du Hoc à Grandcamp*, 1885. The Tate, London.

Photo Credit : Tate, London / Art Resource, NY

(fig. 4)

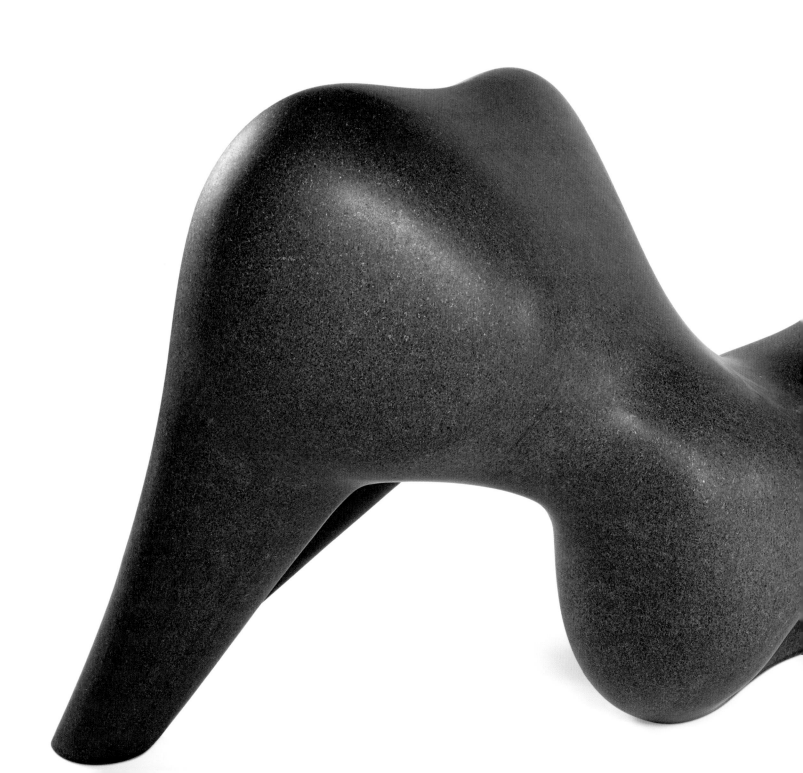

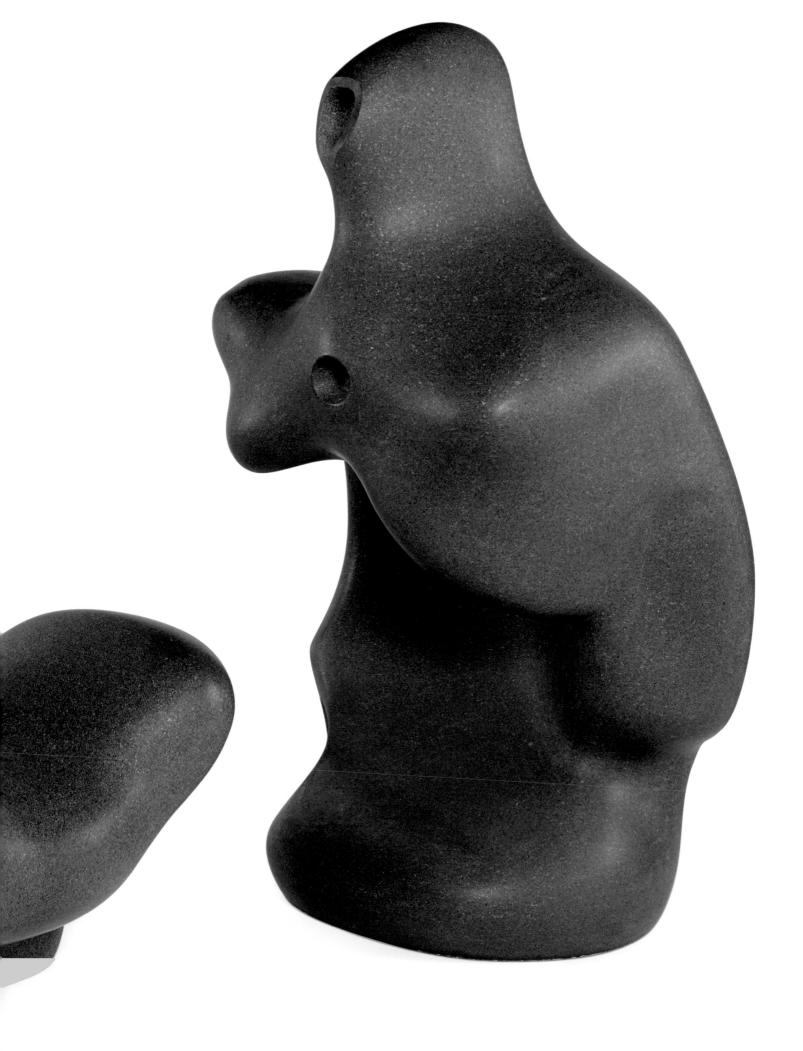

62 HENRY MOORE (1898-1986)

Arch Form

black serpentine marble
Length: 98⅛ in. (249.2 cm.)
Executed in 1970; unique

$5,500,000-7,500,000

PROVENANCE:
Mary Moore (by descent from the artist).
Acquired from the above by the present owner,
1990.

EXHIBITED:
Paris, Galerie Didier Imbert, *Henry Moore Intime*,
April-July 1992, p. 136 (illustrated).
Tokyo, Sezon Museum of Art; Kitakyushu Municipal
Museum of Art; Hiroshima City Museum of
Contemporary Art and The Oita Prefectural Museum
of Art, *Henry Moore Intime*, September 1992-
Auguste 1993, p. 111, no. I-9 (illustrated).
Dallas Museum of Art; Fine Arts Museum of San
Francisco and Washington, D.C., The National
Gallery of Art, *Henry Moore: Sculpting the 20th
Century*, February 2001-January 2002, p. 311,
no. 91 (illustrated in color, p. 235).

LITERATURE:
A. Bowness, ed., *Henry Moore: Sculpture 1964-
1973*, London, 1971, vol. 4, p. 61, no. 618
(illustrated, p. 60; illustrated again, pls. 166-169).
D. Mitchinson, ed., *Henry Moore Sculpture*, London,
1981, p. 239, no. 512 and 513 (illustrated in color).
A.G. Wilkinson, *Henry Moore Remembered: The
Collection at the Art Gallery of Ontario in Toronto*,
exh. cat., 1987, p. 238 (illustrated).

(fig. 1)

(fig. 2)

Arch Form is the largest, most drastically pared down sculpture that Moore ever carved in stone. This uniquely carved, black marble shape is especially rich in associations; its slightly bowed form, asymmetrically stepped and knoblike at both ends, may be likened to a piece of driftwood polished by salty corrosion of ocean waves, a root or log blackened by fire, or a prehistoric bone fossilized over time.

Executed in 1970, *Arch Form* may appear to have had some timely relevance to contemporary developments in sculpture in America: one cannot help noticing that it possesses a decidedly "minimalist" aspect. However, one must be careful here to use the term "minimalist" with a lower-case "m," for the reason that in most ways this radically

(fig. 1) Henry Moore, *Reclining Figure*, 1937. Private collection. Photograph from the archives of the Henry Moore Foundation.
(fig. 2) Henry Moore *Large Torso: Arch*, 1962-63. Photograph from the archives of the Henry Moore Foundation.

reduced shape actually has little if anything in common with the constructivist sources and geometrical tendency that characterize the sculptures of Tony Smith, Robert Morris, Carl André, Donald Judd and Richard Serra, whose work came of age in the 1960s. One might detect in *Arch Form* Moore's subtle response, shaped by the organic principle that he had made his guiding light as far back as the 1920s, to the anti-expressive simplification of form that a half-century later fostered Minimalism, which would eventually prove to be the final notable modernist movement of his century before pluralism took over the contemporary art scene. Whether or not this was something Moore had on his mind, we do not know, for while it is interesting to consider *Arch Form* in light of these issues, it is more by way of comparison, and it is not essential to understanding this work and it sources. Moore's reasons for making it stemmed from a life in art and a vision most entirely his own; it was the product of a career that was then in its full-blown autumnal glory, as the sculptor worked far from the madding crowd.

Imagine the form of this sculpture running below ground in a continuous loop, like the proverbial serpent biting its tail—this will suggest how Moore nearing the end of his career was connecting with his beginnings. *Arch Form* recalls the simple spareness of certain early reclining figures (Lund Humphries, no. 178; fig. 1), although nothing he did during the 1920s and 30s is as sensually sinuous and serpentine as this sculpture. Moore, nevertheless, warned against simplicity as end in itself, which he

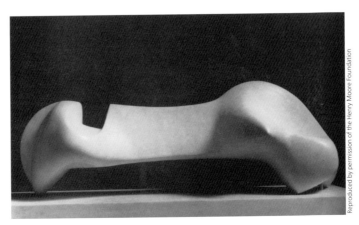

(fig. 3)

believed "tends to emptiness and monotony, but simplicity in carving, interpreted as a lack of surface trimmings, reveals the contrast in section, axis, direction and bulk between different shapes and so intensifies the three-dimensional power in a work." He took as his ideal the work of the primitive carver who "simplifies, I think, through directness of emotional aim to intensify their expression" (quoted in A. Wilkinson, ed., *Henry Moore: Writings and Conversations*, Berkeley, 2002, p. 190). As a result, Moore observed that "All art is an abstraction to some degree: in sculpture the material alone forces one away from pure representation and towards abstraction. Abstract qualities of design are essential to the value of the work, but to me of equal importance is the psychological, human element. If both abstract and human elements are welded together in a work, it must have a fuller, deeper meaning" (quoted in *ibid.*, p. 192).

David Sylvester grouped Moore's subjects into thirteen overlapping categories, beginning with the Reclining Women, the theme that the sculptor treated most frequently (see lots 10 and 18). One may approach *Arch Form* from the vantage point of two such groupings, "Correspondences" (in a general sense) and "Stones, Bones, Shells" (more specifically). Sylvester wrote:

"Going abstract was primarily a consequence of the Brancusi revolution. Brancusi's 'special mission', as Moore saw it, had been to eliminate an overgrowth in European sculpture since the Gothic of 'all sorts of surface excrescences which completely concealed shape.' If shape were to be reasserted, it could be more conspicuous if the sculpture presented itself as a more autonomous entity. Furthermore, this entity could be given a form that would evoke a multiplicity of associations and so imply the notion of metamorphosis—a possibility with which Brancusi was concerned only intermittently, if at all, but which became central for Arp and Miró and Tanguy, for Picasso at moments, and for Moore. Free association produces signficant results when congruity of structure is discovered in things or situations which are incongruous in their character or context" (in *Henry Moore*, exh. cat., The Tate Gallery, London, 1968, p. 35, 36).

Moore listed the broadest possible field of sources for these associations:

"THE WHOLE OF NATURE—BONES, PEBBLES, SHELLS, CLOUDS, TREE TRUNKS, FLOWERS—ALL IS GRIST TO THE MILL OF A SCULPTURE. PEOPLE HAVE THOUGHT—THE LATER GREEKS, IN THE HELLENISTIC PERIOD—THAT THE HUMAN FIGURE WAS THE ONLY SUBJECT, THAT IT ENDED THERE; A QUESTION OF COPYING. BUT I BELIEVE IT'S A QUESTION OF METAMORPHOSIS. WE MUST RELATE THE HUMAN FIGURE TO ANIMALS, TO CLOUDS, TO THE LANDSCAPE—BRING THEM ALL TOGETHER. THERE'S NO DIFFERENCE BETWEEN THEM ALL. BY USING THEM LIKE METAPHORS IN POETRY, YOU GIVE NEW MEANING TO THINGS" (QUOTED IN A. WILKINSON, ED., *OP. CIT.*, PP. 221-222).

Some of these associations were drawn from Moore's earliest memories of how he responded to forms in nature. He recalled: "In Yorkshire in Adel Woods just outside Leeds, there was a big rock amongst many that I've called Adel Rock. That influenced me quite a bit. For me, it was the first big, bleak lump of stone set in a landscape and surrounded by marvelous gnarled prehistoric trees. It had no feature of recognition, no element of copying of naturalism, just bleak, powerful form, very impressive. It was the local beauty spot, so to speak, and I knew it from a child. And much later, when I was a student, I would visit it with friends. We would picnic and draw and play around. It was an exciting place for me, Adel Woods" (quoted in J. Hedgecoe, ed., *Henry Moore: My Ideas, Inspiration and Life as an Artist*, London, 1986, p. 35).

(fig. 4) Durdle Door, near Lulworth in Dorset.
(fig. 5) Landscape Arch, Arches National Park, Utah.

No less memorable was Stonehenge, which Moore first visited in the fall of 1921. "As it was a clear evening I got to Stonehenge and saw it by moonlight," he later wrote. "I was alone and terribly impressed. (Moonlight, as you know, enlarges everything, and the mysterious depths and distance made it seem enormous. I went again the next morning, it was still very impressive, but that first moonlight visit remained for ideas my idea of Stonehenge" (quoted in A. Wilkinson, ed., *op. cit.*, p. 49).

The first arch sculpture that Moore created is *Large Torso: Arch*, 1962-1963 (Lund Humphries, no. 503; fig. 2). Its monumental scale and basic shape, consisting of two tall uprights linked by a continuous but twisting and knotted transverse segment, recalls the basic structure of the Stonehenge and a Romanesque arch, but note how Moore has transformed these architectural elements into to an expressively anthropomorphic form. He wrote in his notebooks in 1941, "I myself in my work tend to humanise everything, to relate mountains to people, tree trunks to the human body, pebbles to heads & figures, etc." (quoted in *ibid.*, p. 114). In a discussion that same year with novelist V. S. Pritchett, the painter Graham Sutherland and renowned art historian Sir Kenneth Clark, Moore stated, "In almost all of my carvings there has been an organic idea in my mind. I think of it as having a head, body, limbs, and as the piece of stone or wood I carve evolves from the first roughing-out stages it begins to take on a definite human personality and character. And to bring the work to its final conclusion involves one's whole psychological make-up and whatever one can draw upon and make use of from the sum of one's human and form experience" (quoted in *ibid.*, p. 126).

Around 1928-1929 Moore began to make a habit of collecting pebbles, shells and bones. He drew them in his sketchbooks, and studied them in exhibitions. In an interview with Arnold L. Haskell in 1932, he stated, "I have studied the principles of organic growth in the bones and shells at the Natural History Museum and have found new form and rhythm to apply go sculpture. Of course one does not just copy the form of a bone, say, into stone, but applies the principles of construction, variety, transition of one

(fig. 6)

form into another, to some other subject—with me nearly always the human form, for that is what interests me—so giving, as the image and metaphor do in poetry, a new significance to each" (quoted in *ibid.*, p.189).

Trees also suggested sculptural forms, in ways similar to bones. "Bones have a marvelous sculptural strength and hard tenseness of form, subtle transition from one shape into the next and great variety in section," he wrote. "Trees (tree trunks) show principles of growth and strength of joints, with easy passing of one section in the next" (*ibid.*, p. 192). Aspects of both may be found in *Arch Form*. Moore had already created a *Reclining Form* in 1966 with a pronounced bone-like appearance (Lund Humphries, no. 557; fig. 3), which is also in the shape of a flattened arch.

Also related to the arch is the bridge form, such as that seen in the leg section of *Two Piece Reclining Figure Number Two*, 1960, one of Moore's earliest sectioned recumbent women. Naturally occurring arch and bridge forms were a source for these shapes. There is the famous limestone Durdle Door on the Dorset coast near Lulworth (fig. 4). Moore cited the Manneporte at Etretat on the Normandy coast, famously painted by Courbet and Monet, as an important precedent of natural forms providing inspiration for artists. Americans are likely to think of the extraordinary natural rock structures in Arches National Park in Utah, including the seemingly impossible attenuated form of Landscape Arch (fig. 5) in the Devil's Garden, in the north side of the park.

The arch form in architecture, like most man-made structural elements, is static in its purely geometrical and symmetrical state. Moore observed in notes he wrote in 1950 that "A straight line, a pure curve, solid geometrical forms, a perfect sphere, cone, cylinders, cubes are thought to be beautiful—(Plato) but they can be best made by machines, not artists—Art shows the fallible, human variations from the perfect" (quoted *ibid.*, 114). Moore's *Arch Form*, on the other hand, is asymmetrical: it is slightly higher on one side than the other, and slopes gently along its length, and each end of the sculpture, where the form breaks downward as if to enter the ground, differs from the other. Moore wrote in 1934, "Asymmetry is connected also with the desire for the organic (which I have) rather than the geometric" (quoted in *ibid.*, p. 191). The effect of asymmetry gives Arch Form the appearance of a striding motion, of one leg placed before the other. Of all Rodin's sculpture Moore most admired *L'homme qui marche*: "I like its springiness, tautness and energy The forms diverge upwards from the ankle to the knee and from the knee to the top of the thigh. This gives an upward thrust..." (quoted in *ibid.*, pp. 182-83).

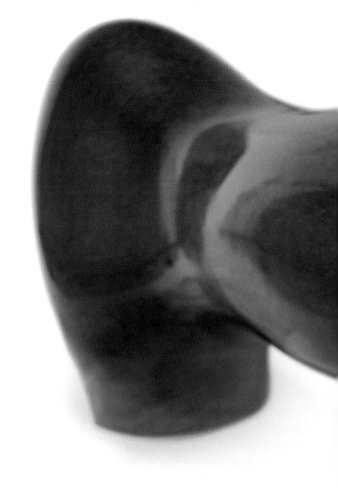

It is in fact the leg-like aspect of *Arch Form*, a shape akin to the human femur, that induced Moore to use this element as the leg segment in the two-piece *Reclining Figure: Arch Leg*, which he cast in bronze, also in 1969-1970 (Lund Humphries, no. 610; fig. 6). However many allusions this evocative form may conjure up, in the end it is embodiment of a tensile strength, a force that the pulses through the arching stone. Moore wrote in 1964:

"ONE OF THINGS I WOULD LIKE TO THINK MY SCULPTURE HAS IS A FORCE, IS A STRENGTH, IS A LIFE, A VITALITY FROM INSIDE IT, SO THAT YOU HAVE A SENSE THAT THE FORM IS PRESSING FROM INSIDE, TRYING TO BURST OR GIVE OFF STRENGTH FROM INSIDE ITSELF, RATHER THAN HAVING SOMETHING WHICH IS JUST SHAPED FROM OUTSIDE AND IS STOPPED. IT'S AS THOUGH YOU HAVE SOMETHING TRYING TO MAKE ITSELF COME TO A SHAPE FROM INSIDE ITSELF. THIS IS PERHAPS WHAT MAKES ME INTERESTED IN BONES AS MUCH AS IN FLESH BECAUSE THE BONE IS THE INNER STRUCTURE OF ALL LIVING FORM. IT'S THE BONE THAT PUSHES OUT FROM INSIDE; AS YOU BEND YOUR LEG YOUR KNEE GETS A TAUTNESS OVER IT, AND IT'S THERE THAT THE MOVEMENT AND ENERGY COME FROM" (QUOTED IN *IBID.*, PP. 198-199).

66 HENRY MOORE (1898-1986)

Working Model for Seated Woman

signed and numbered 'Moore 7/9' (on the top of the base);
inscribed with foundry mark 'H. NOACK BERLIN' (on the back of the base)
bronze with golden brown patina
Height: 31⅞ in. (80.9 cm.)
Conceived in 1980 and cast in the artist's lifetime

$1,500,000-2,000,000

PROVENANCE:

Jeffrey H. Loria & Co., Inc., New York (acquired from the artist).
Acquired from the above by the present owner, *circa* 1993.

LITERATURE:

A. Bowness, ed., *Henry Moore: Complete Sculpture 1955-1964*, London, 1986, vol. 3, p. 36, no. 433b (another cast illustrated; another cast illustrated again pls. 66-67).

© The Trustees of the British Museum

(fig. 1) *The Chamberlain Inyotef, son of Senet.* Limestone figure of the Twelfth Dynasty, *circa* 1950 BC. British Museum, London.

In 1960, while being interviewed by Edouard Roditi, Moore touched the bronze cast of the 1957 version of *Seated Woman* (Lund Humphries, no. 435) which he had set in the meadow outside his Hertfordshire home, and reminisced, "Whenever I see this figure, I am reminded of a boyhood experience that contributed to the conception of its form. I was a Yorkshire miner's son, the youngest of seven, and my mother was no longer so very young. She suffered from bad rheumatism in the back and would often say to me in winter, when I came home from school: 'Henry, boy, come and rub my back.' Then I would massage her back with liniment. When I came to model this figure which represents a fully mature woman, I found that I was unconsciously giving to its back the long-forgotten shape of the one that I had rubbed as a boy" (quoted in A. Wilkinson, ed., *Henry Moore: Writings and Conversations*, Berkeley, 2002, p. 32).

Moore created approximately twenty-four related versions of the imposing *Seated Woman* between 1952 and 1986. The stalwart matriarchal character of Moore's *Seated Woman* is a testament to his beloved mother, whose presence in his life, even after her death in 1944, became an especially memory-charged touchstone for a distinctive type of presentation among the sculptor's manifold evocations of the female body. "She was to me the absolute stability, the rock, the whole thing in life that one knew was there for one's protection," Moore recalled of his mother, "so it's not surprising that the women have this kind of feeling and that the kind of women I've done in sculpture are mature women rather than young" (quoted in *ibid.*, p. 33). Moore's memories of his mother, reawakened through the embodied sensation of touch, linger in the austere corporeality of this *Working Model for Seated Woman*. The hardness of the bronze and the frontality of her pose positively suggest the fortitude and monumental repose that consistently distinguish his female figures. "Tactile experience is very important as an aesthetic dimension in sculpture," Moore once remarked, and in the present work he heightens the expressivity of the body through the contrast between the smoothness and roundedness of the figure's back and upper torso and the subtle modeling of the drapery around her legs (quoted in *ibid.*, p. 210). The folds of the drapery clarify the sculptural idea of the figure, articulating its shape and stressing the grounded solidity of her physical presence.

The quality of stillness and the strong frontality that characterize many of Moore's *Seated Women* from this time (Lund Humphries 418a, 428, 431) bear similarities to the ancient Egyptian figures that had first captivated his sculptural imagination years earlier. Describing a seated Egyptian figure (fig. 1) to the photographer David Finn, Moore acclaimed, "This piece shows tremendously fine observation of the human figure. The back is equally good—strong, taut and poised. The whole figure has the stillness I particularly associate with the Egyptians, a stillness of waiting, not of death" (quoted in D. Finn, ed., *Henry Moore in the British Museum*, New York, 1981, p. 35). Moore's renewed attention to antique sources from Egypt, Etruria, and the primitive Mediterranean world connect him to what Christa Lichtenstern has described as a pervasive "search for a new humanism triggered by the horror of the Second World War." Like many of his postwar contemporaries, Moore sought "a new beginning based on the creative legacy of Antiquity," a desire that complemented the manifest humanism long inherent in his work (in M. Fath, "Henry Moore: The Path to Maturity," *Henry Moore: From the Inside Out, Plasters, Carvings and Drawings*, exh. cat., Muse des Beaux-Arts, Nantes, 1996, p. 23). As Moore revisited the *Seated Woman* near the end of his career, he emphasized the simple grandeur of the figure; the surface of her body is smooth and softly burnished with a golden brown patina. Moore never departed from his belief that "in the human figure one can express more completely one's feelings about the world than in any other way," (quoted in A. Wilkinson, *op. cit.*, p. 221). In *Working Model for Seated Woman* he again affirmed the resilience of the human spirit, and singled out for praise, on behalf of all flesh born of woman, the towering and majestic, yet compassionate, all-wise and protective maternal body.

HENRY MOORE (1898-1986)

Reclining Figure: External Form

bronze with green patina
Length: 86¾ in. (220.3 cm.)
Conceived in 1953-1954 and cast in 1957

$4,500,000-6,000,000

PROVENANCE:

Mary Moore (by descent from the artist).
Acquired from the above by the present owner,
1990.

EXHIBITED:

Paris, Didier Imbert Fine Art, *Henry Moore Intime*,
April-July 1992, pp. 150-151 (illustrated in color).
Tokyo, Sezon Museum of Art, *Henry Moore Intime*,
September-November 1992, p. 113 (illustrated).
Windermere, Isleworth Golf Course, October 2006-
May 2008.

LITERATURE:

W. Grohmann, *The Art of Henry Moore*, London,
1960, nos. 48 and 49 (another cast illustrated).
J. Hedgecoe, ed., *Henry Moore*, New York, 1968, p.
329 (another cast illustrated; another cast illustrated
again, p. 331).
R. Melville, *Henry Moore: Sculpture and Drawings
1921-1969*, London, 1970, nos. 480 and 481
(another cast illustrated).
D. Mitchinson, ed., *Henry Moore Sculpture*, London,
1981, p. 118, no. 236 (another cast illustrated).
A. Bowness, ed., *Henry Moore: Sculpture 1949-
1954*, London, 1986, vol. 2, p. 36, no. 299 (another
cast illustrated; another cast illustrated again pls. 68-
75).
Exh. cat., *Henry Moore: Sculpting the 20th Century*,
Dallas Museum of Art, 2001, pp. 16-19 (another
cast illustrated).

(fig. 1)

(fig. 2)

(fig. 1) Henry Moore, *Working Model for Reclining Figure: External Form*, 1951. Photograph from the archives of the Henry Moore Foundation. (fig. 2) Henry Moore, *Two Forms*, carved wood, 1934. The Museum of Modern Art, New York. Photograph from the archives of the Henry Moore Foundation.

Reclining Figure: External Form outwardly displays the general and familiar character of Moore's many Reclining Figures. The figure is cast in the asymmetrical layout typical of this series, with the taller part of figure representing the upper body at one end, which then declines into the midsection and legs on the other. There are also Moore's signature holes (see lot 14), four in all, and indeed these gaping voids of cut into the mass of this sculpture is as important to the conception of this work as the bronze which makes up the rest of it. These large holes form openings into a vast interior cavity, an empty volume. This sculpture is in effect a large and contorted enclosure, or a cocoon of sorts, a bronze shell which in fact once held within it a separate interior form. Moore explained:

"This large reclining figure is called 'External Form.' The working model [Lund Humphries, no. 298; fig. 1] has an interior piece, and in translating it into full size the internal form was also included. The two forms were of course, made separately, although I continuously fitted them together and related the shapes to each other. Later I decided the external form made a better sculpture on its own. The interesting result for me is that the interior form remains by implication" (quoted in J. Hedgecoe, *op. cit.*, p. 200).

John Russell described the erstwhile interior piece as "a vulnerable, tuber-like form." He suspected that Moore felt "there was something basically abhorrent to him in the invalidish forms of the projected internal piece." Russell declared that in the final version, the sculpture as seen here, "the vacant inner spaces set up some of the grandest echoes in all Moore" (*op. cit.*, pp. 148-149).

Even if one were not aware that the working model originally included an internal piece, it becomes immediately apparent that the enclosed negative space implies and even defines an absence, that is, an missing 'presence'. This inference—the 'recollection' of the missing form— is an idea which is crucial to understanding and appreciating what it is that actually remains as a hard material presence. This conjunction of negative space and positive mass, of forms that describe both presence and absence, is marvelously Zen in its coexistential contradictions: if this sculpture resists to some degree one's accustomed experience of a Moore Reclining Figure as a palpably sensual feminine body, it nevertheless suggests a contemplatively cerebral approach to the apprehension of plastic form that is no less seductive and rewarding.

Reclining Figure: External Form thus represents one side in the dialogue between two opposing but complementary ideas; it is the outer element in the important thematic category of Moore's work which the sculptor, as well as his commentators, have characterized as Internal and External Forms. In a 1980 conversation with David Mitchinson, Moore recalled the origins of this idea:

"THE IDEA OF ONE FORM INSIDE ANOTHER FORM MAY OWE SOME OF ITS INCIPIENT BEGINNINGS TO MY INTEREST AT ONE STAGE WHEN I DISCOVERED ARMOUR. I SPENT MANY HOURS IN THE WALLACE COLLECTION, IN LONDON, LOOKING AT ARMOUR. NOW ARMOUR IS AN OUTSIDE SHELL LIKE THE SHELL OF A SNAIL WHICH IS THERE TO PROTECT THE MORE VULNERABLE FORMS INSIDE, AS IT IS IN HUMAN ARMOUR WHICH IS HARD AND PUT ON TO PROTECT THE SOFT BODY. THIS HAS LED SOMETIMES TO THE IDEA OF THE MOTHER AND CHILD WHERE THE OUTER FORM, THE MOTHER, IS PROTECTING THE INNER FORM, THE CHILD, LIKE A MOTHER DOES PROTECT HER CHILD" (QUOTED IN A. WILKINSON, *HENRY MOORE: WRITINGS AND CONVERSATIONS*, BERKELEY, 2002, PP. 213-214).

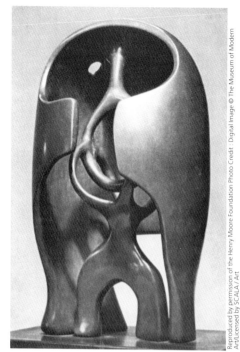

(fig. 3)

(fig. 4)

Moreover, as the sculptor recounted elsewhere: "It may be that I remembered reading stories that impressed me and Wyndham Lewis talking about the shell of a lobster covering the soft flesh inside. This became an established idea with me—that of an outer protection to an inner form, and it may have something to do with the mother and child idea; that is where there is the relation of the big thing to the little thing, and the protection idea. The helmet is a kind of protection thing, too, and it became a recording of things inside other things. The mystery of semi-obscurity where can only half distinguish something. In the helmet you do not quite know what is inside" (quoted in *ibid.*, p. 214).

The pierced and enveloping forms of *Reclining Figure: External Form* have their earliest precedent in *Two Forms*, 1934 (Lund Humphries, no. 153, fig. 2), in which a curved, hollowed out form appears about to envelope a smaller stone-like shape, as if either to protect it or, more sinisterly, to consume it. Moore's first actual foray into Internal and External Forms was *The Helmet*, 1939-1940 (Lund Humphries, no. 212; fig. 3). Here a hollow form styled after an ancient Greek helmet, with its pronounced cheek-guards, protectively embraces a spindly, rather fragile-looking openwork figure within. Moore explored this idea various sketch-book pages during 1947-1948, and in 1950 he made more Helmet Heads (Lund Humphries, nos. 278-281 and 283). Russell has traced the shifting emphasis in these works from an obviously military source, influenced by the recent global conflict and the ensuing Cold War, to another more typical and warmly intimate theme for Moore, the Mother and Child:

"Within the fulfilled and rounded form is its antithesis, a form that is angular, irregular, uneasy, often forked and frantic. Nature itself set the tone by making the skull one of the more regular and predictable of known objects, and the skull's contents so absolutely erratic and mysterious. Moore from the first gave his outer covering the grand flawless outline of a Greek helmet: what sits within is various enough for the findings of psychiatry... Once inside the outer covering it can never be seen complelely: when not inside, it looks incomplete and defenceless. The combined figures are, in short, nearer to mother and child, or to mother and foetus, than to any manual of warfare" (*op. cit.*, pp. 139-140).

(fig. 3) Henry Moore, *The Helmet*, 1939-1940. Photograph from the archives of the Henry Moore Foundation.
(fig. 4) Henry Moore, *Internal and External Forms*, 1953-1954. Albright-Knox Art Gallery, Buffalo. Photograph from the archives of the Henry Moore Foundation.

(fig. 5)

Reproduced by permission of the Henry Moore Foundation

This idea is clearly apparent in the most impressive of Moore internal/external sculptures, the carved elmwood *Internal and External Forms*, 1953-1954 (Lund Humphries, no. 297; fig. 4), which Moore worked on while creating the present sculpture. This vertical conflation of forms compelled the psychiatrist Erich Neumann to write:

"What we see here is the mother bearing the still-unborn child within her and holding the born child again in her embrace. But this child is the dweller within the body, the psyche itself, for which the body, like the world, is merely the circumambient space that shelters or casts out. It is no accident that this figure reminds us of those Egyptian sarcophagi in the form of mummies, showing the mother goddess as the sheltering womb that holds and contains the dead man like a child again, as at the beginning. Mother of life, mother of death, and all-embracing body-self, the archetypal mother of man's ego consciousness—this truly great sculpture of Moore's is all these in one" (quoted in *ibid.*, pp. 143 and 145).

Moore executed *Reclining Mother and Child* in 1960-1961 (Lund Humphries, no. 480; fig. 5). Rather than filling the length of the external form, here a more compact form of the child is cradled within the embrace of the mother's upper body. David Sylvester noted that "The form it assumes suggests the common infantile fantasy of associating babies inside women's bodies with penises inside women's bodies The child form is powerfully ambiguous—at once explosively aggressive and a blunt huddled baby animal. The mother appears from the front to be nursing it, retaining it, from the back to be giving birth, expelling it (in *Henry Moore*, exh. cat., Tate Gallery, London, 1968, p. 85).

In comparing these related sculptures, the fascinating variety of allusions in the internal/external dialectic becomes apparent, and reveals Moore as the consummate poet of forms, for as he said, "we express one thing in the image of another" (quoted in S. Compton, *Henry Moore*, exh. cat., Royal Academy of Arts, London, 1988, p. 259). It seemed inevitable then, that he should create a work in which the external form has shed the internal element, and indeed he was right in doing this, because the resultant sculpture is in no way less complete or convincing than if had included the internal part. He has simply, and most profoundly, conjured up the presence of the internal form by boldly declaring its absence. The internal entity has been expelled, leaving a still-swollen vacuity behind. Moore has traced an elemental natural process through the expression in forms, in which he lays out, through the power of suggestion, an extended narrative, the timeline of an organic evolution that extends from conception through pregnancy, birth and its aftermath. In addition to the three dimensions of its physicality, *Reclining Figure: External Form* also suggests the fourth dimension of time, perceived through the faculty of memory, which cannot help but summon up the recollection of the interior form which, as he stated, "remains by implication".

The present cast of *Reclining Figure: External Form* is the artist's proof, formerly owned by the artist's daughter Mary. It is the only example of the seven cast which has remained in private hands. The six casts in the edition are located in the following museums: (1) Toledo Museum of Art, Ohio (2) Israel Museum, Jerusalem, (3) University of Freiburg, Germany, (4) Galleria Nazionale d'Arte Moderna, Rome, (5) Museum of Fine, Richmond, Virginia, and (6) Museo Nacional de Bellas Artes, Buenos Aires.

(fig. 5) Henry Moore, *Reclining Mother and Child*, 1960-1961. Sold, Christie's New York, 19 November 1998, lot 366.

INTERNATIONAL IMPRESSIONIST, 20TH CENTURY AND CONTEMPORARY ART DEPARTMENTS

INTERNATIONAL DIRECTORS
Martha Baer
(Post-War and Contemporary Art)
Tel: +1 212 636 2071
Guy Bennett
(Impressionist and Modern Art)
Tel: +1 212 636 2056
Florence de Botton
(Post-War and Contemporary Art)
Tel: +33 1 40 76 84 15
Amy Cappellazzo
(Post-War and Contemporary Art)
Tel: +1 212 636 2339
Brett Gorvy
(Post-War and Contemporary Art)
Tel: +1 212 636 2342
John Lumley
(Impressionist and Modern Art)
Tel: +44 (0)20 7389 2055
Laura Paulson
(Post-War and Contemporary Art)
Tel: +1 212 636 2134
Jussi Pylkkänen
(Impressionist and Modern Art)
Tel: +44 (0)20 7389 2452
Andreas Rumbler
(Impressionist and Modern Art)
Tel: +49 (0)211 49 15 93 13
Thomas Seydoux
(Impressionist and Modern Art)
Tel: +33 (0)1 40 76 86 18

HONORARY CHAIRMAN, AMERICAS
Christopher Burge
Tel: +1 212 636 2910

INTERNATIONAL BUSINESS DIRECTORS
Jennifer Zatorski
(Impressionist and Modern Art)
Tel: +1 212 468 7148
Emmanuel de Chaunac
(Post-War and Contemporary Art)
Tel: +33 1 40 76 83 67

BUSINESS MANAGERS
AMERICAS
Post-War & Contemporary
Julie Kim
Tel: +1 212 636 2317
LONDON AND EUROPEAN
Bart van Son
Tel: +44 (0)20 7389 2094

Post-War & Contemporary, King Street
Zoe Ainscough
Tel: +44 (0)20 7389 2958
ART ADVISORY ASIAN CLIENTS
Ken Yeh, Deputy Chairman, Asia
Tel: +1 212 636 2063
JAPANESE CLIENT LIAISON
Keiko Yagishita
Tel: +1 212 636 2248

WORLDWIDE
AMSTERDAM
Jetske Homan van der Heide
Arno Verkade
Tel: +31 (0)20 575 5282
BRUSSELS
Tel: +32 2 289 13 35
DUSSELDORF
Herrad Schorn
Tel: +49 (0)211 49 15 93 13
GENEVA
Nadja Scribante Amstutz
Tel: +41 (0)22 319 17 13
HONG KONG
Eric Chang
Tel: +852 2978 9985
LONDON (KING STREET)
IMPRESSIONIST AND MODERN ART
Giovanna Bertazzoni
Jay Vincze
Liberté Nuti
Matthew Stephenson
Teresa Krasny
Valerie Didier
Tel: +44 (0)20 7389 2449
POST-WAR AND CONTEMPORARY ART
Pilar Ordovas
Jean-Paul Engelen
Lock Kressler
Dina Amin
Alice de Martigny
Jeremy Goldsmith
Guya Bertoni
Anne-Sophie Villemin
Tel: +44 (0)20 7389 2958
LONDON (SOUTH KENSINGTON)
IMPRESSIONIST AND MODERN ART
Deborah Park
India Phillips
Tel: +44 (0)20 7752 3218
POST-WAR AND CONTEMPORARY ART
Lindsey Gallen
Darren Leak
Yuki Baumgarten
Tel: +44 (0)20 7752 3313
LOS ANGELES
Zach Miner
Tel: +1 310 385 2659
MADRID
María García Yelo
Tel: +34 91 532 6627
MILAN
Giulio Sangiuliano
Federica Gavazzi
Tel: +39 02 303 283 30

NEW YORK
IMPRESSIONIST AND MODERN ART
Guy Bennett
Cyanne Chutkow
Sheri Farber
Conor Jordan
Sharon Kim
Liz Clark
Brooke Lampley
Stefany Sekara
Amy Albright
Jessica Fertig
Maxwell Carter
Caroline Hayward
Tel: +1 212 636 2050
POST-WAR AND CONTEMPORARY ART
Robert Manley
Andrew Massad
Ingrid Dudek
Jonathan Laib
Alexandre Carel
April Jacobs
Marley Lewis
Sara Friedlander
Jennifer Rohr
Tel: +1 212 636 2100
PARIS
Christophe Durand-Ruel
Anika Guntrum
Laetitia Bauduin
Marine Bancilhon
Jean-Olivier Despres
Elodie Morel
Michael Gumener
Tel: +33 (0)1 40 76 86 18
ROME
Mariolina Bassetti
Renato Pennisi
Tel: +39 06 686 33 30
SYDNEY
Tel: +612 93 26 14 22
TEL AVIV
Roni Gilat-Baharaff
Tel: +97 23 695 0695
TOKYO
Kanae Ishibashi
Toshihiko Hatanaka
Keiichi Takemura
Tel: +81 3 35 71 06 68
ZURICH
Hans-Peter Keller
Rene Lahn
Tel: +41 (0)44 268 1010

Email. First initial followed by last name@christies.com (eg. Martha Baer = mbaer@christies.com)

INTERNATIONAL IMPRESSIONIST, 20TH CENTURY AND CONTEMPORARY ART AUCTIONS

TO INCLUDE YOUR PROPERTY IN THESE SALES PLEASE CONSIGN TEN WEEKS BEFORE THE SALE DATE.
CONTACT THE SPECIALISTS OR REPRESENTATIVE OFFICE FOR FURTHER INFORMATION.

2 OCTOBER
SUBASTA DE ARTE ESPAÑOL
MADRID

13 OCTOBER
PHOTOGRAPHS
NEW YORK

14 OCTOBER
PHOTOGRAPHS
NEW YORK

19 OCTOBER
POST WAR & CONTEMPORARY
LONDON, KING STREET

20 OCTOBER
ITALIAN ART
LONDON, KING STREET

21 OCTOBER
POST WAR & CONTEMPORARY
LONDON, KING STREET

28 OCTOBER
PRINTS
NEW YORK

30 OCTOBER
INTERNATIONAL MODERN & CONTEMPORARY ART
DUBAI

11 NOVEMBER
PHOTOGRAPHS
LONDON, KING STREET

5 NOVEMBER
IMPRESSIONIST & MODERN ART
NEW YORK

6 NOVEMBER
IMPRESSIONIST & MODERN ART
NEW YORK

6 NOVEMBER
IMPRESSIONIST & MODERN ART
NEW YORK

12 NOVEMBER
POST WAR & CONTEMPORARY
NEW YORK

13 NOVEMBER
POST WAR & CONTEMPORARY
NEW YORK

13 NOVEMBER
POST WAR & CONTEMPORARY
NEW YORK

19 NOVEMBER
PRINTS & MULTIPLES
LONDON, SOUTH KENSINGTON

20 NOVEMBER
PHOTOGRAPHS
LONDON, SOUTH KENSINGTON

24 NOVEMBER
ARTE MODERNA E CONTEMPORANEA
MILAN

1 DECEMBER
ART IMPRESSIONNISTE ET MODERNE
PARIS

1 DECEMBER
SWISS ART
ZURICH

2 DECEMBER
OLD MASTER PRINTS
LONDON, KING STREET

2 DECEMBER
20TH CENTURY ART
AMSTERDAM

9 & 10 DECEMBER
ART D'APRÈS-GUERRE ET CONTEMPORAIN
PARIS

10 DECEMBER
IMPRESSIONIST & MODERN ART
LONDON, SOUTH KENSINGTON

11 DECEMBER
POST WAR & CONTEMPORARY
LONDON, SOUTH KENSINGTON

IMPORTANT NOTICES AND EXPLANATION OF CATALOGUING PRACTICE

CHRISTIE'S INTEREST IN PROPERTY CONSIGNED FOR AUCTION

From time to time, Christie's may offer a lot which it owns in whole or in part. Such property is identified in the catalogue with the symbol Δ next to its lot number.

On occasion, Christie's has a direct financial interest in lots consigned for sale which may include guaranteeing a minimum price or making an advance to the consignor that is secured solely by consigned property. Such property is identified in the catalogue by the symbol ° next to the lot number. This symbol will be used both in cases where Christie's holds the financial interest on its own, and in cases where Christie's has financed all or a part of such interest through a third party. Such third parties generally benefit financially if a guaranteed lot is sold successfully and may incur a loss if the sale is not successful. The financing offered by a third party may be in the form of an irrevocable bid provided by that third party. Where Christie's has an ownership or financial interest in every lot in the catalogue, Christie's will not designate each lot with a symbol, but will state its interest at the front of the catalogue.

ALL DIMENSIONS ARE APPROXIMATE

CONDITION REPORTS

Christie's catalogues include references to condition only in descriptions of multiple works (such as prints, books and wine). For all other property, only alterations or replacement components are listed. Please contact the Specialist Department for a condition report on a particular lot.

Condition reports are provided as a service to interested clients. Prospective buyers should note that descriptions of property are not warranties and that each lot is sold "as is."

PROPERTY INCORPORATING MATERIALS FROM ENDANGERED SPECIES

An export license issued by the US Fish and Wildlife Service will be required for the export of any item made of or incorporating (irrespective of percentage) fish and wildlife material such as ivory, whalebone, rhinoceros horn, tortoiseshell, rosewood or coral. Such works have been marked with two asterisks (★★). Prospective purchasers are advised that several countries prohibit altogether the importation of property containing such materials. Accordingly, clients should familiarize themselves with relevant customs regulations prior to bidding if they intend to import this lot into another country.

It is the obligation of the seller to know and to satisfy the requirements of all laws protecting a particular species, whether plant or wildlife, whose parts or products are intended for sale through Christie's. In this regard, Christie's is prohibited by law from possessing, exhibiting, offering for sale or selling property incorporating certain protected plant or wildlife materials and products. These prohibited materials include, but are not limited to, certain categories of ivory and tortoiseshell, as well as most North American bird feathers and eggs. It is very important that any person who wishes to sell property through Christie's containing plant or wildlife materials consult with a Christie's specialist before turning the property over to Christie's. In certain cases, Christie's may be required by law to hand over property containing protected plant or wildlife materials to government officials, who could impose a fine on the seller and/or require that the seller forfeit the property. Prior to delivering any property to Christie's, potential sellers should be prepared to provide Christie's with any and all documentation and certificates of exemption as may be required by any federal or state law.

FOR PICTURES, DRAWINGS, PRINTS AND MINIATURES

1. PABLO PICASSO

In Christie's opinion a work by the artist.

2. Attributed to PABLO PICASSO★

In Christie's qualified opinion a work of the period of the artist which may be in whole or part the work of the artist.

3. After PABLO PICASSO★

In Christie's qualified opinion a copy of the work of the artist.

4. 'signed'

Has a signature which in Christie's qualified opinion is the signature of the artist.

5. 'bears signature'

Has a signature which in Christie's qualified opinion might be the signature of the artist.

6. 'dated'

Is so dated and in Christie's qualified opinion was executed at about that date.

7. 'bears date'

Is so dated and in Christie's qualified opinion may have been executed at about that date.

★This term and its definition in this Explanation of Cataloguing Practice are a quaified statement as to Authorship. While the use of this term is based upon careful study and represents the opinion of experts, Christie's and the consignor assume no risk, liability and responsibility for the authenticity of authorship of any lot in this catalogue described by this term.

23/11/05

CONDITIONS OF SALE

Christie's Conditions of Sale and Limited Warranty are set out later in this catalogue Bidders are strongly encouraged to read these as they set out the terms on which property is bought at auction.

ESTIMATES

Estimates are based upon prices recently paid at auction for comparable property, condition, rarity, quality and provenance. Estimates are subject to revision. Buyers should not rely upon estimates as a representation or prediction of actual selling prices. Estimates do not include the buyer's premium or VAT. Where "Estimate on Request" appears, please contact the Specialist Department for further information.

RESERVES

The reserve is the confidential minimum price the consignor will accept and will not exceed the low pre-sale estimate. Lots that are not subject to a reserve are identified by the symbol • next to the lot number.

BUYER'S PREMIUM

Christie's charges a premium to the buyer on the final bid price of each lot sold at the following rates: 25% of the final bid price of each lot up to and including $50,000, 20% of the excess of the hammer price above $50,000 and up to and including $1,000,000 and 12% of the excess of the hammer price above $1,000,000.
Exceptions:
Wine: 20% of the final bid price of each lot sold. For all lots, taxes are payable on the premium at the applicable rate.

PRE-AUCTION VIEWING

Pre-auction viewings are open to the public free of charge. Christie's specialists are available to give advice and condition reports at viewings or by appointment.

BIDDER REGISTRATION

Prospective buyers who have not previously bid or consigned with Christie's should bring:
• Individuals: government-issued photo identification (such as a driving licence, national identity card, or passport) and, if not shown on the ID document, proof of current address, for example a utility bill or bank statement.
• Corporate clients: a certificate of incorporation.
• For other business structures such as trusts, offshore companies or partnerships, please contact Christie's Credit Department at +1 212 636 2492 for advice on the information you should supply.
• A financial reference in the form of a recent bank statement, a reference from your bank, and/or your banker's contact information. Christie's can supply a form of wording for the bank reference if necessary.
• Persons registering to bid on behalf of someone who has not previously bid or consigned with Christie's should bring identification documents not only for themselves but also for the party on whose behalf they are bidding, together with a signed letter of authorization from that party.
To allow sufficient time to process the information, new clients are encouraged to register at least 48 hours in advance of a sale.
Prospective buyers should register for a numbered bidding paddle at least 30 minutes before the sale. Clients who have not made a purchase from any Christie's office within the last two years and those wishing to spend more than on previous occasions, will be asked to supply a new bank reference to register.
For assistance with references, please contact Christie's Credit Department at +1 212 636 2490 or by fax at +1 212 636 4943.

REGISTERING TO BID ON SOMEONE ELSE'S BEHALF

Persons bidding on behalf of an existing client should bring a signed letter from the client authorizing the bidder to act on the client's behalf. Please note that Christie's does not accept payments from third parties. Christie's can only accept payment from the client, and not from the person bidding on their behalf.

BIDDING

The auctioneer accepts bids from those present in the saleroom, from telephone bidders, or by absentee written bids left with Christie's in advance of the auction. The auctioneer may also execute bids on behalf of the seller up to the amount of the reserve. The auctioneer will not specifically identify bids placed on behalf of the seller. Under no circumstances will the auctioneer place any bid on behalf of the seller at or above the reserve. Bid steps are shown on the Absentee Bid Form at the back of this catalogue.

ABSENTEE BIDS

Christie's staff will attempt to execute an absentee bid at the lowest possible price taking into account the reserve price. Absentee bids submitted on "no reserve" lots will, in the absence of a higher bid, be executed at approximately 50% of the low pre sale estimate or at the amount of the bid if it is less than 50% of the low pre-sale estimate. The auctioneer may execute absentee bids directly from the rostrum, clearly identifying these as "absentee bids," "book bids," "order bids" or "commission bids." Absentee Bids Forms are available in this catalogue, at any Christie's location or online at christies.com.

TELEPHONE BIDS

Telephone bids will be accepted for lots with low-end estimates of $1,500 and above, no later than 24 hours prior to the sale and only if the capacity of our pool of staff phone bidders allows.
Arrangements to bid in languages other than English must be made well in advance of the sale date.

Telephone bids may be recorded. By bidding on the telephone, prospective purchasers consent to the recording of their conversations.

Christie's offers all absentee and telephone bidding services as a convenience to our clients, but will not be responsible for errors or failures to execute bids.

SUCCESSFUL BIDS

While invoices are sent out by mail after the auction, we do not accept responsibility for notifying you of the result of your bids. Buyers are requested to contact us by telephone or in person as soon as possible after the sale to obtain details of the outcome of their bids to avoid incurring unnecessary storage charges. Successful bidders will pay the price of the final bid plus premium plus any applicable taxes.

PAYMENT

Under normal circumstances, you are expected to pay for your purchases within seven calendar days of the sale and to remove the property you have bought by that date. Payment may be made by personal check, bank wire transfers, cash (in US currency up to $7,500), Travelers checks (in US currency up to $7,500) and money orders (in US currency up to $7,500). To avoid delivery delays, prospective buyers are encouraged to supply bank or other suitable references before the auction.
Please note that Christie's will not accept payments for purchased Lots from any party other than the buyer, unless otherwise agreed between the buyer and Christie's prior to the sale.

SALES TAX

Purchases picked up in New York or delivered to locations in California, Connecticut, District of Columbia, Florida, Illinois, Massachusetts, New Jersey, New York, Pennsylvania, Rhode Island or Texas may be subject to sales or compensating use tax of such jurisdiction.
Christie's is selling lots designated by a star (★) as agent for an organization which holds a State of New York Exempt Organization Certificate. Accordingly, no sales tax is due on the purchase price of any of the foregoing lots if the property is picked up or delivered in the State of New York. However, a compensating use tax is due from the buyer if any such lot is shipped to New Jersey or Connecticut or any of the following states where Christie's maintains offices: California, Florida, Illinois, Massachusetts, Pennsylvania, Rhode Island, Texas and District of Columbia.
It is the buyer's responsibility to ascertain and pay all taxes due. Buyers claiming exemption from sales tax must have the appropriate documentation on file with Christie's prior to the release of the property. For more information, please contact Purchaser Payments at +1 212 636 2496.

COLLECTION OF PURCHASED LOTS

Buyers are expected to remove their property within 7 calendar days of the auction. Please consult the Pick-Up Information Sheet for collection information for purchased lots. This sheet is available from the Bidder Registration staff, Purchaser Payments or the Packing Desk.

SHIPPING

A shipping form is enclosed with each invoice. It is the buyer's responsibility to pick up purchases or make all shipping arrangements. After payment has been made in full, Christie's can arrange property packing and shipping at the buyer's request and expense. Where Christie's arranges and bills for such services via invoice or credit card, an administration charge will apply. We recommend that buyers request an estimate for any large items or property of high value that require professional packing. For more information please contact the Art Transport Department at +1 212 636 2480.
We regret that Christie's staff will not accommodate requests to roll canvases sold on stretchers.

EXPORT/IMPORT PERMITS

Property sold at auction may be subject to laws governing export from the US and import restrictions of foreign countries. Buyers should always check whether an export license is required before exporting. It is the buyer's sole responsibility to obtain any relevant export or import license. The denial of any license or any delay in obtaining licenses shall neither justify the rescission of any sale nor any delay in making full payment for the lot. Upon request, Christie's will assist the buyer in submitting applications to obtain the appropriate licenses. However, Christie's cannot ensure that a license will be obtained. Local laws may prohibit the import of some property and/or may prohibit the resale of some property in the country of importation, no such restriction shall justify the rescission of any sale or delay in making full payment for the lot. If a license is obtained on a buyer's behalf, a minimum fee of $150 per item will be charged. For more information, please contact the Art Transport Department at +1 212 636 2480.

12/7/07

STORAGE AND COLLECTION

STORAGE AND COLLECTION

All lots will be stored free of charge for 35 days from the auction date at Christie's or, at Christie's option, at Cadogan Tate Fine Art Storage Ltd at 41-19 38th Street, Long Island City, NY 11101, +1 718 706 7999. Lots are available for collection from either location during any working day from 9.30 am to 4.30 pm. (Lots may not be collected during the day of their move to Cadogan Tate or to Christie's warehouse in Long Island City.) Please consult the Pick-Up Information Sheet for collection information. This sheet is available from the Bidder Registration staff, Purchaser Payments or the Packing Desk and will be sent with your invoice.

STORAGE CHARGES

After 35 days from the auction date, property shall incur the following charges plus any applicable sales tax due:

INSURANCE

Insurance is charged at the lesser of the amount of the aggregate charges incurred for storage or at the rate of 0.6% of the insured value of the property, including premium, or, at Cadogan Tate's option, the property's repair or replacement value.

Lots will not be released until all outstanding charges due to Christie's and Cadogan Tate are settled. Please contact Cadogan Tate at +1 718 706 7999 and Christie's Purchaser Payments at +1 212 636 2496 to ascertain any amounts due. Property valued at over $250,000 may not be eligible for the Cadogan Tate program.

Charges	Furniture/ Large Objects	Pictures/ Small Objects
Administration	$100.00	$50.00
Storage (per day)	$10.00	$5.00

STREET MAP OF CHRISTIE'S NEW YORK LOCATIONS

Christie's Rockefeller Center
20 Rockefeller Plaza, New York 10020
Tel: +1 212 636 2000
Main Entrance on 49th Street
Receiving/Shipping
Entrance on 48th Street

Cadogan Tate
41-19 38th Street, Sunnyside,
NY 11101,
Tel: +1 718 706 7999

LIC Warehouse
13–06 43rd Avenue,
Long Island City NY 11101
Tel: +1 718 361 6340
Entrance on 13th Street

CONDITIONS OF SALE

These Conditions of Sale and the Important Notices and Explanation of Cataloguing Practice contain all the terms on which Christie's and the seller contract with the buyer. They may be amended by posted notices or oral announcements made during the sale. By bidding at auction you agree to be bound by these terms.

1. CHRISTIE'S AS AGENT
Except as otherwise stated Christie's acts as agent for the seller. The contract for the sale of the property is therefore made between the seller and the buyer.

2. BEFORE THE SALE
(a) Examination of property
Prospective buyers are strongly advised to examine personally any property in which they are interested, before the auction takes place. Condition reports are usually available on request. Neither Christie's nor the seller provides any guarantee in relation to the nature of the property apart from the Limited Warranty in paragraph 6 below. The property is otherwise sold "as is."

Our cataloguing practice is explained in the Important Notices and Explanation of Cataloguing Practice after the catalogue entries. All statements by us in the catalogue entry for the property or in the condition report, or made orally or in writing elsewhere, are statements of opinion and are not to be relied on as statements of fact. Such statements do not constitute a representation, warranty or assumption of liability by us of any kind. References in the catalogue entry or the condition report to damage or restoration are for guidance only and should be evaluated by personal inspection by the bidder or a knowledgeable representative. The absence of such a reference does not imply that an item is free from defects or restoration, nor does a reference to particular defects imply the absence of any others. Estimates of the selling price should not be relied on as a statement that this is the price at which the item will sell or its value for any other purpose. Except as set forth in paragraph 6 below, neither Christie's nor the seller is responsible in any way for errors and omissions in the catalogue or any supplemental material.

(c) Buyer's responsibility
Except as stated in the Limited Warranty in paragraph 6 below, all property is sold "as is" without any representation or warranty of any kind by Christie's or the seller. Buyers are responsible for satisfying themselves concerning the condition of the property and the matters referred to in the catalogue entry.

3. AT THE SALE
(a) Refusal of admission
Christie's has the right, at our complete discretion, to refuse admission to the premises or participation in any auction and to reject any bid.

(b) Registration before bidding
A prospective buyer must complete and sign a registration form and provide identification before bidding. We may require the production of bank or other financial references.

(c) Bidding as principal
When making a bid, a bidder is accepting personal liability to pay the purchase price, including the buyer's premium and all applicable taxes, plus all other applicable charges, unless it has been explicitly agreed in writing with Christie's before the commencement of the sale that the bidder is acting as agent on behalf of an identified third party acceptable to Christie's, and that Christie's will only look to the principal for payment.

(d) Absentee bids
We will use reasonable efforts to carry out written bids delivered to us prior to the sale for the convenience of clients who are not present at the auction in person, by an agent or by telephone. Bids must be placed in the currency of the place of the sale. Please refer to the catalogue for the Absentee Bids Form. If we receive written bids on a particular lot for identical amounts, and at the auction these are the highest bids on the lot, it will be sold to the person whose written bid was received and accepted first. Execution of written bids is a free service undertaken subject to other commitments at the time of the sale and we do not accept liability for failing to execute a written bid or for errors and omissions in connection with it.

(e) Telephone bids
Telephone bids will be accepted for lots with low-end estimates of $1,500 and above, no later than 24 hours prior to the sale and only if the capacity of our pool of staff phone bidders allows. Arrangements to bid in languages other than English must be made well in advance of the sale date.
Telephone bids may be recorded. By bidding on the telephone, prospective purchasers consent to the recording of their conversations.
Christie's offers all absentee and telephone bidding services as a convenience to our clients, but will not be responsible for errors or failures to execute bids.

(f) Currency converter
At some auctions a currency converter may be operated. Errors may occur in the operation of the currency converter and we do not accept liability to bidders who follow the currency converter rather than the actual bidding in the saleroom.

(g) Video or digital images
At some auctions there may be a video or digital screen. Errors may occur in its operation and in the quality of the image and we do not accept liability for such errors.

(h) Reserves
Unless otherwise indicated, all lots are offered subject to a reserve, which is the confidential minimum price below which the lot will not be sold. The reserve will not exceed the low estimate printed in the catalogue. If any lots are not subject to a reserve, they will be identified with the symbol ∗ next to the lot number. The auctioneer may open the bidding on any lot below the reserve by placing a bid on behalf of the seller. The auctioneer may continue to bid on behalf of the seller up to the amount of the reserve, either by placing consecutive bids or by placing bids in response to other bidders. With respect to lots that are offered without reserve, unless there are already competing bids, the auctioneer, in his or her discretion, will generally open the bidding at 50% of the low pre-sale estimate for the lot. In the absence of a bid at that level, the auctioneer will proceed backwards in his or her discretion until a bid is recognized, and then continue up from that amount. Absentee bids will, in the absence of a higher bid, be executed at approximately 50% of the low pre-sale estimate or at the amount of the bid if it is less than 50% of the low pre-sale estimate. In the event that there is no bid on a lot, the auctioneer may deem such lot unsold.

(i) Auctioneer's discretion
The auctioneer has the right at his absolute and sole discretion to refuse any bid, to advance the bidding in such a manner as he may decide, to withdraw or divide any lot, to combine any two or more lots and, in the case of error or dispute, and whether during or after the sale, to determine the successful bidder, to continue the bidding, to cancel the sale or to reoffer and resell the item in dispute. If any dispute arises after the sale, our sale record is conclusive.

(j) Successful bid and passing of risk
Subject to the auctioneer's discretion, the highest bidder accepted by the auctioneer will be the buyer and the striking of his hammer marks the acceptance of the highest bid and the conclusion of a contract for sale between the seller and the buyer. Risk and responsibility for the lot (including frames or glass where relevant) passes to the buyer at the expiration of seven calendar days from the date of the sale or on collection by the buyer if earlier.

4. AFTER THE SALE
(a) Buyer's premium
In addition to the hammer price, the buyer agrees to pay to us the buyer's premium together with any applicable value added tax, sales or compensating use tax or equivalent tax in the place of sale. The buyer's premium is 25% of the final bid price of each lot up to and including $50,000, 20% of the excess of the hammer price above $50,000 and up to and including $1,000,000 and 12% of the excess of the hammer price above $1,000,000.

(b) Payment and passing of title
Immediately following the sale, the buyer must provide us with his or her name and permanent address and, if so requested, details of the bank from which payment will be made. The buyer must pay the full amount due (comprising the hammer price, buyer's premium and any applicable taxes) not later than 4.30pm on the seventh calendar day following the sale. This applies even if the buyer wishes to export the lot and an export license is, or may be, required. The buyer will not acquire title to the lot until all amounts due to us from the buyer have been received by us in good cleared funds even in circumstances where we have released the lot to the buyer.

(c) Collection of purchases
We shall be entitled to retain items sold until all amounts due to us, or to Christie's International plc, or to any of its affiliates, subsidiaries or parent companies worldwide, have been received in full in good cleared funds or until the buyer has satisfied such other terms as we, in our sole discretion, shall require, including, for the avoidance of doubt, completing any anti-money laundering or anti-terrorism financing checks we may require to our satisfaction. In the event a buyer fails to complete any anti-money laundering or anti-terrorism financing checks to our satisfaction, Christie's shall be entitled to cancel the sale and to take any other actions that are required or permitted under applicable law. Subject to this, the buyer shall collect purchased lots within seven calendar days from the date of the sale unless otherwise agreed between us and the buyer.

(d) Packing, handling and shipping
Although we shall use reasonable efforts to take care when handling, packing and shipping a purchased lot, we are not responsible for the acts or omissions of third parties whom we might retain for these purposes. Similarly, where we may suggest other handlers, packers or carriers if so requested, we do not accept responsibility or liability for their acts or omissions.

(e) Export licence
Unless otherwise agreed by us in writing, the fact that the buyer wishes to apply for an export license does not affect his or her obligation to make payment within seven days nor our right to charge interest or storage charges on late payment. If the buyer requests us to apply for an export license on his or her behalf, we shall be entitled to make a charge for this service. We shall not be obliged to rescind a sale nor to refund any interest or other expenses incurred by the buyer where payment is made by the buyer in circumstances where an export license is required.

12/7/07

(f) Remedies for non payment

If the buyer fails to make payment in full in good cleared funds within the time required by paragraph 4(b) above, we shall be entitled in our absolute discretion to exercise one or more of the following rights or remedies (in addition to asserting any other rights or remedies available to us by law):

(i) to charge interest at such rate as we shall reasonably decide;

(ii) to hold the defaulting buyer liable for the total amount due and to commence legal proceedings for its recovery together with interest, legal fees and costs to the fullest extent permitted under applicable law;

(iii) to cancel the sale;

(iv) to resell the property publicly or privately on such terms as we shall think fit;

(v) to pay the seller an amount up to the net proceeds payable in respect of the amount bid by the defaulting buyer;

(vi) to set off against any amounts which we, or Christie's International plc, or any of its affiliates, subsidiaries or parent companies worldwide, may owe the buyer in any other transactions, the outstanding amount remaining unpaid by the buyer;

(vii) where several amounts are owed by the buyer to us, or to Christie's International plc, or to any of its affiliates, subsidiaries or parent companies worldwide, in respect of different transactions, to apply any amount paid to discharge any amount owed in respect of any particular transaction, whether or not the buyer so directs;

(viii) to reject at any future auction any bids made by or on behalf of the buyer or to obtain a deposit from the buyer before accepting any bids;

(ix) to exercise all the rights and remedies of a person holding security over any property in our possession owned by the buyer, whether by way of pledge, security interest or in any other way, to the fullest extent permitted by the law of the place where such property is located. The buyer will be deemed to have granted such security to us and we may retain such property as collateral security for such buyer's obligations to us;

(x) to take such other action as we deem necessary or appropriate.

If we resell the property under paragraph (iv) above, the defaulting buyer shall be liable for payment of any deficiency between the total amount originally due to us and the price obtained upon resale as well as for all costs, expenses, damages, legal fees and commissions and premiums of whatever kind associated with both sales or otherwise arising from the default. If we pay any amount to the seller under paragraph (v) above, the buyer acknowledges that Christie's shall have all of the rights of the seller, however arising, to pursue the buyer for such amount.

(g) Failure to collect purchases

Where purchases are not collected within seven calendar days from the date of the sale, whether or not payment has been made, we shall be permitted to remove the property to a third party warehouse at the buyer's expense, and only release the items after payment in full has been made of removal, storage, handling, insurance and any other costs incurred, together with payment of all other amounts due to us.

(h) Selling Property at Christie's

In addition to expenses such as transport and insurance, all consignors pay a commission according to a fixed scale of charges based upon the value of the property sold by the consignor at Christie's in a calendar year. Commissions are charged on a sale by sale basis.

5. EXTENT OF CHRISTIE'S LIABILITY

We agree to refund the purchase price in the circumstances of the Limited Warranty set out in paragraph 6 below. Apart from that, neither the seller nor we, nor any of our officers, employees or agents, are responsible for the correctness of any statement of whatever kind concerning any lot, whether written or oral, nor for any other errors or omissions in description or for any faults or defects in any lot. Except as stated in paragraph 6 below, neither the seller, ourselves, our officers, employees or agents, give any representation, warranty or guarantee or assume any liability of any kind in respect of any lot with regard to merchantability, fitness for a particular purpose, description, size, quality, condition, attribution, authenticity, rarity, importance, medium, provenance, exhibition history, literature or historical relevance. Except as required by local law any warranty of any kind whatsoever is excluded by this paragraph.

6. LIMITED WARRANTY

Subject to the terms and conditions of this paragraph, Christie's warrants for a period of five years from the date of the sale that any property described in headings printed in UPPER CASE TYPE (i.e. headings having all capital-letter type) in this catalogue (as such description may be amended by any saleroom notice or announcement) which is stated without qualification to be the work of a named author or authorship, is authentic and not a forgery. The term "author" or "authorship" refers to the creator of the property or to the period, culture, source or origin, as the case may be, with which the creation of such property is identified in the UPPER CASE description of the property in this catalogue. Only UPPER CASE TYPE headings of lots in this catalogue indicate what is being warranted by Christie's. Christie's warranty does not apply to supplemental material which appears below the UPPER CASE TYPE headings of each lot and Christie's is not responsible for any errors or omissions in such material. The terms used in the headings are further explained in Important Notices and Explanation of Cataloguing Practice. The warranty does not apply to any heading which is stated to represent a qualified opinion. The warranty is subject to the following:

(i) It does not apply where (a) the catalogue description or saleroom notice corresponded to the generally accepted opinion of scholars or experts at the date of the sale or fairly indicated that there was a conflict of opinions; or (b) correct identification of a lot can be demonstrated only by means of either a scientific process not generally accepted for use until after publication of the catalogue or a process which at the date of publication of the catalogue was unreasonably expensive or impractical or likely to have caused damage to the property.

(ii) The benefits of the warranty are not assignable and shall apply only to the original buyer of the lot as shown on the invoice originally issued by Christie's when the lot was sold at auction.

(iii) The original buyer must have remained the owner of the lot without disposing of any interest in it to any third party.

(iv) The buyer's sole and exclusive remedy against Christie's and the seller, in place of any other remedy which might be available, is the cancellation of the sale and the refund of the original purchase price paid for the lot. Neither Christie's nor the seller will be liable for any special, incidental or consequential damages including, without limitation, loss of profits nor for interest.

(v) The buyer must give written notice of claim to us within five years from the date of the auction. It is Christie's general policy, and Christie's shall have the right, to require the buyer to obtain the written opinions of two recognized experts in the field, mutually acceptable to Christie's and the buyer, before Christie's decides whether or not to cancel the sale under the warranty.

(vi) The buyer must return the lot to the Christie's saleroom at which it was purchased in the same condition as at the time of the sale.

7. COPYRIGHT

The copyright in all images, illustrations and written material produced by or for Christie's relating to a lot including the contents of this catalogue, is and shall remain at all times the property of Christie's and shall not be used by the buyer, nor by anyone else, without our prior written consent. Christie's and the seller make no representation or warranty that the buyer of a property will acquire any copyright or other reproduction rights in it.

8. SEVERABILITY

If any part of these Conditions of Sale is found by any court to be invalid, illegal or unenforceable, that part shall be discounted and the rest of the conditions shall continue to be valid to the fullest extent permitted by law.

9. LAW AND JURISDICTION

The rights and obligations of the parties with respect to these Conditions of Sale, the conduct of the auction and any matters connected with any of the foregoing shall be governed and interpreted by the laws of the jurisdiction in which the auction is held. By bidding at auction, whether present in person or by agent, by written bid, telephone or other means, the buyer shall be deemed to have submitted, for the benefit of Christie's, to the exclusive jurisdiction of the courts of that country, state, county or province, and (if applicable) of the federal courts sitting in such state.

5/2/07

WORLDWIDE SALEROOMS AND OFFICES

ARGENTINA

BUENOS AIRES
+54 11 43 93 42 22
Cristina Carlisle

AUSTRALIA

MELBOURNE
+61 (0)3 9820 4311
Patricia Kontos
SYDNEY
+61 (0)2 9326 1422
Ronan Sulich

AUSTRIA

VIENNA
+43 (0)1 533 8812
Angela Baillou

BELGIUM

BRUSSELS
+32 (0)2 512 88 30
Roland de Lathuy

BERMUDA

BERMUDA
+1 401 849 9222
Betsy Ray

BRAZIL

RIO DE JANEIRO
+5521 2225 6553
Candida Sodre
SÃO PAULO
+5511 3081 0435
Christina Haegler

CANADA

TORONTO
+1 416 960 2063
Erica House

CHILE

SANTIAGO
+562 263 1642
Denise Ratinoff de Lira

CZECH REPUBLIC

PRAGUE
+420 724 008 980
Nicole Stava
(Consultant)

DENMARK

COPENHAGEN
+45 (0)39 62 23 77
Rikke Juel
(Consultant)

FINLAND AND THE BALTIC STATES

HELSINKI
+358 (0)9 608 212
Barbro Schauman
(Consultant)

FRANCE

BORDEAUX
+33 (0)5 56 81 65 47
Marie-Cécile Moueix
LILLE
+33 (0)6 60 97 82 36
Laurence Lalart
(Consultant)
LYON
+33 (0)6 72 72 96 37
MARSEILLE / AIX EN PROVENCE
+33 (0)4 91 72 29 40
Fabienne Albertini-Cohen
(Consultant)
NANTES
+33 (0)6 09 44 90 78
Virginie Greggory
(Consultant)
• PARIS
+33 (0)1 40 76 85 85
TOULOUSE
+33 (0)6 87 40 99 91
Florence Grassignoux
(Consultant)

GERMANY

BERLIN
+49 (0)30 88 56 95 30
Viktoria von Specht
DÜSSELDORF
+49 (0)21 14 91 59 30
Andreas Rumbler
FRANKFURT
+49 (0)61 74 20 94 85
Anja Becker
HAMBURG
+49 (0)40 27 94 073
Christiane Gräfin zu Rantzau
MUNICH
+49 (0)89 24 20 96 80
Marie Christine Gräfin Huyn
STUTTGART
+49 (0)71 12 26 96 99
Eva Susanne Schweizer

GREECE

ATHENS
+30 210 672 9248
Lisa Melas (Consultant)

INDIA

MUMBAI
+91 22 2280 7905
Ganieve Grewal

INDONESIA

JAKARTA
+6221 7278 6268
Amalia Wirjono

ISRAEL

• TEL AVIV
+972 (0)3 695 0695
Roni Gilat-Baharaff

ITALY

• MILAN
+39 02 303 2831
ROME
+39 06 686 3333
NORTH ITALY
+39 348 3131 021
Paola Gradi
(Consultant)
VENICE
+39 041 277 0086
Bianca Arrivabene Valenti Gonzaga
(Consultant)
BOLOGNA
+39 051 265 154
Benedetta Possati Vettori Venenti
(Consultant)
GENOA
+39 010 246 3747
Rachele Guicciardi
(Consultant)
FLORENCE
+39 055 219 012
Alessandra Niccolini di Camugliano (Consultant)
CENTRAL & SOUTHERN ITALY
+39 348 520 2974
Alessandra Allaria
(Consultant)
TURIN
+39 02 303 28354
Sandro Perrone di San Martino (Consultant)

JAPAN

TOKYO
+81 (0)3 3571 0668
Kanae Ishibashi

MALAYSIA

KUALA LUMPUR
+60 3 2070 8837
Lim Meng Hong

MEXICO

MEXICO CITY
+52 55 5281 5503
Gabriela Lobo

MONACO

+377 97 97 11 00
Nancy Dotta
(Consultant)

THE NETHERLANDS

• AMSTERDAM
+31 (0)20 57 55 255
ROTTERDAM
+31 (0)10 212 0553
Hyldeke Vrolijk
(Consultant)

NORWAY

OSLO
+47 22 06 56 96
Aase Bach (Consultant)

PEOPLES REPUBLIC OF CHINA

BEIJING
+86 (0)10 6500 6517
Jane Shan
• HONG KONG
+852 2521 5396
SHANGHAI
+86 (0)21 6279 8773
Harriet Yu

PORTUGAL

LISBON
+351 (0)919 317 233
Mafalda Pereira Coutinho (Consultant)

• **DENOTES SALEROOM**   **ENQUIRIES**— Call the Saleroom or Office   **EMAIL**— info@christies.com
For a complete salerooms & offices listing go to christies.com

9/05/07

RUSSIA

MOSCOW
+7 495 937 3075
+44 20 7389 2318
Anna Belorusova

SINGAPORE

SINGAPORE
+65 6235 3828
Wen Li Tang

SOUTH AFRICA

+27 (0)21 761 2676
Juliet Lomberg
(Consultant)

SOUTH KOREA

SEOUL
+82 2 720 5266
Hye-Kyung Bae

SPAIN

BARCELONA
+34 (0)93 487 8259
Cuca Escoda
• **MADRID**
+34 (0)91 532 6626
Juan Varez

SWITZERLAND

• **GENEVA**
+41 (0)22 319 1766
Eveline de Proyart
• **ZURICH**
+41 (0)44 268 1010
Dr. Dirk Boll

TAIWAN

TAIPEI
+886 2 2736 3356
Ada Ong

THAILAND

BANGKOK
+66 2 652 1097
Yaovanee Nirandara

TURKEY

ISTANBUL
+90 (0)532 582 4895
Zeynep Kayhan
(Consultant)

UNITED ARAB
EMIRATES

• **DUBAI**
+971 (0)4 425 5647
Shanti Veigas

UNITED KINGDOM

• **LONDON**
+44 (0)20 7839 9060
LONDON,
• **SOUTH KENSINGTON**
+44 (0)20 7930 6074
SOUTH
+44 (0)845 900 1766
Mark Wrey
The Earl Fortescue
(Consultant)
NORTH
+44 (0)845 900 1766
Thomas Scott
Richard Compton
(Consultant)
EAST
+44 (0)845 900 1766
Charles Bingham-
Newland
Simon Reynolds
Thomas Fellowes
(Consultant)
**NORTH-WEST AND
WALES**
+44 (0)845 900 1766
Mark Newstead

SCOTLAND
+44 (0)131 225 4756
Bernard Williams
Robert Lagneau
Grant MacDougall
David Bowes-Lyon
(Consultant)
ISLE OF MAN
+44 1624 814502
The Marchioness
Conyngham
(Consultant)
CHANNEL ISLANDS
+44 (0)1534 485 988
Melissa Bonn

IRELAND

+353 (0)59 86 24996
Christine Ryall

UNITED STATES

BOSTON
+1 617 536 6000
Elizabeth M. Chapin
CHICAGO
+1 312 787 2765
Steven J. Zick
DALLAS
+1 214 599 0735
Capera Ryan
HOUSTON
+1 713 802 0191
Lisa Cavanaugh
• **LOS ANGELES**
+1 310 385 2600
MIAMI
+1 305 445 1487
Vivian Pfeiffer
NEWPORT
+1 401 849 9222
Betsy D. Ray
• **NEW YORK**
+1 212 636 2000
PALM BEACH
+1 561 833 6952
Meg Bowen
PHILADELPHIA
+1 610 520 1590
Alexis McCarthy
SAN FRANCISCO
+1 415 982 0982
Martine Krumholz
WASHINGTON, D.C.
+1 202 333 7459
Cathy Sledz

For a complete salerooms & offices listing go to christies.com

5/9/072

CHRISTIE'S SPECIALIST DEPARTMENTS AND SERVICES

DEPARTMENTS

AFRICAN AND OCEANIC ART
PAR: +33 (0)140 768 386

AMERICAN DECORATIVE ARTS
NY: +1 212 636 2230

AMERICAN FURNITURE
NY: +1 212 636 2230

AMERICAN INDIAN ART
NY: +1 212 468 7137

AMERICAN PICTURES
NY: +1 212 636 2140

ANGLO-INDIAN ART
KS: +44 (0)20 7389 2570

ANTIQUITIES
NY: +1 212 636 2245

ARMS AND ARMOUR
KS: +44 (0)20 7389 2020

AUSTRALIAN PICTURES
KS: +44 (0)20 7389 2040

BOOKS AND MANUSCRIPTS
NY: +1 212 636 2665

BRITISH & IRISH ART
KS: +44 (0)20 7389 2682
NY: +1 212 636 2084
SK: +44 (0)20 7752 3257

BRITISH ART ON PAPER
KS: +44 (0)20 7389 2278
SK: +44 (0)20 7752 3293
NY: +1 212 636 2084

BRITISH PICTURES 1500-1850
KS: +44 (0)20 7389 2945

CAMERAS AND OPTICAL TOYS
SK: +44 (0)20 7752 3279

CARPETS
NY: +1 212 636 2217

CERAMICS AND GLASS
NY: +1 212 636 2215

CHINESE PAINTINGS
NY: +1 212 636 2195

CHINESE WORKS OF ART
NY: +1 212 636 2180

CLOCKS
KS: +44 (0)20 7389 2224

COLLECTIBLES
NY: +1 212 636 2272

CORKSCREWS
SK: +44 (0)20 7752 3263

COSTUME, TEXTILES AND FANS
SK: +44 (0)20 7752 3215

DOLLS
SK: +44 (0)20 7752 3276

ENTERTAINMENT MEMORABILIA
NY: +1 212 636 2272

FOLK ART
NY: +1 212 636 2230

FURNITURE
NY: +1 212 636 2200

HOUSE SALES
SK: +44 (0)20 7752 3260

ICONS
SK: +44 (0)20 7752 3261

IMPRESSIONIST AND MODERN ART
NY: +1 212 636 2050

INDIAN AND SOUTHEAST ASIAN ART
NY: +1 212 636 2190

INDIAN CONTEMPORARY ART
NY: +1 212 636 2189
KS: +44 (0)20 7389 2700

INTERIORS
NY: +1 212 636 2032
SK: +44 (0)20 7389 2236

ISLAMIC WORKS OF ART
KS: +44 (0)20 7389 2370
SK: +44 (0)20 7752 3239

JAPANESE ART
NY: +1 212 636 2160
KS: +44 (0)20 7389 2591

JEWELLERY
NY: +1 212 636 2300

KOREAN ART
NY: +1 212 636 2165

LATIN AMERICAN ART
NY: +1 212 636 2150

MARITIME
NY: +1 212 707 5949

MECHANICAL MUSIC
SK: +44 (0)20 7752 3278

MINIATURES
NY: +1 212 636 2250

MODERN DESIGN
SK: +44 (0)20 7389 2142

MUSICAL INSTRUMENTS
NY: +1 212 707 5974

NINETEENTH CENTURY EUROPEAN PAINTINGS
NY: +1 212 636 2090

NINETEENTH CENTURY FURNITURE AND SCULPTURE
NY: +1 212 707 5910

OBJECTS OF VERTU
NY: +1 212 636 2250

OLD MASTER DRAWINGS
NY: +1 212 636 2115

OLD MASTER PAINTINGS
NY: +1 212 636 2120

PHOTOGRAPHS
NY: +1 212 636 2330

PICTURE FRAMES
SK: +44 (0)20 7389 2763

POST WAR AND CONTEMPORARY ART
NY: +1 212 636 2100

POSTERS
SK: +44 (0)20 7752 3208

PRINTS
NY: +1 212 636 2290

RUSSIAN WORKS OF ART
NY: +1 212 636 2260

SCIENTIFIC INSTRUMENTS
SK: +44 (0)20 7752 3286

SCULPTURE
KS: +44 (0)20 7389 2331
SK: +44 (0)20 7389 2794

SILVER
NY: +1 212 636 2250

SPORTING ART
NY: +1 212 636 2084

SPORTING GUNS
KS: +44 (0)20 7389 2025

TEDDY BEARS
SK: +44 (0)20 7752 3335

TOPOGRAPHICAL PICTURES
KS: +44 (0)20 7389 2040
SK: +44 (0)20 7752 3291

TWENTIETH CENTURY DECORATIVE ART AND DESIGN
NY: +1 212 636 2240

VICTORIAN PICTURES
KS: +44 (0)20 7389 2468
SK: +44 (0)20 7752 3257

WATCHES
NY: +1 212 636 2320

WINE
NY: +1 212 636 2270

AUCTION SERVICES

CHRISTIE'S AUCTION ESTIMATES
Tel: +1 212 636 2615
Fax: +1 212 636 4954
Email: info@christies.com

CHRISTIE'S FINE ART SECURITY SERVICES
UK: +44 (0)20 7622 0609
Fax: +44 (0)20 7978 2073
Email: cfass@christies.com

CORPORATE COLLECTIONS
Tel: +1 212 636 2375
Fax: +1 212 636 2370
Email: sfarber@christies.com

ESTATES AND APPRAISALS
Tel: +1 212 636 2400
Fax: +1 212 636 2370
Email: info@christies.com

FINANCIAL SERVICES
Tel: +1 212 636 2572
Fax: +1 212 492 5467
Email: emcgorry@christies.com

MUSEUM SERVICES
Tel: +1 212 636 2620
Fax: +1 212 636 4931
Email: awhiting@christies.com

OTHER SERVICES

CHRISTIE'S EDUCATION
New York
Tel: +1 212 355 1501
Fax: +1 212 355 7370
Email: christieseducation@christies.edu

London
Tel: +44 (0)20 7665 4350
Fax: +44 (0)20 7665 4351
Email: education@christies.com

Paris
Tel: +33 (0)1 42 25 10 90
Fax: +33 (0)1 42 25 10 91
Email: ChristiesEducationParis@christies.com

CHRISTIE'S GREAT ESTATES
Tel: +1 505 983 8733
Fax: +1 505 982 0348
Email: info@christiesge.com

CHRISTIE'S IMAGES
Tel: +1 718 472 5030
Fax: +1 718 472 9005
Email: imagesny@christies.com

HAUNCH OF VENISON
Robert Fitzpatrick
Tel: +1 212 636 2034
Fax: +1 212 636 4959

KEY TO ABBREVIATIONS
KS:
London, King Street
NY:
New York, Rockefeller Plaza
PAR:
Paris
SK:
London, South Kensington

30/07/07

ABSENTEE BIDS FORM

CHRISTIE'S NEW YORK

HENRY MOORE SCULPTURE IMPRESSIONIST/MODERN EVENING SALE

THURSDAY 6 NOVEMBER 2008
AT 6.30 PM
20 Rockefeller Plaza
New York, NY 10020
CODE NAME: ROCCO
SALE NUMBER: 2045

(Dealers billing name and address must agree with tax exemption certificate. Invoices cannot be changed after they have been printed.)

BID ONLINE FOR THIS SALE AT CHRISTIES.COM

BIDDING INCREMENTS
Bidding generally opens below the low estimate and advances in increments of up to 10%, subject to the auctioneer's discretion. Absentee bids that do not conform to the increments set below may be lowered to the next bidding interval.

$50 to $1,000	by $50s
$1,000 to $2,000	by $100s
$2,000 to $3,000	by $200s
$3,000 to $5,000	by $200, 500, 800
(ie: $4,200, 4,500, 4,800)	
$5,000 to $10,000	by $500s
$10,000 to $20,000	by $1,000s
$20,000 to $30,000	by $2,000s
$30,000 to $50,000	by $2,000, 5,000, 8,000
(ie: $32,000, 35,000, 38,000)	
$50,000 to $100,000	by $5,000s
$100,000 to $200,000	by $10,000s
above $200,000	at auctioneer's discretion

The auctioneer may vary the increments during the course of the auction at his or her own discretion.

Auction Results: +1 212 703 8080

Please also refer to the information contained in Buying at Christie's. I request Christie's to bid on the following lots up to the maximum price I have indicated for each lot. I understand that if my bid is successful, the purchase price will be the sum of my final bid plus a buyer's premium of 25% of the final bid price of each lot up to and including $50,000, 20% of the excess of the hammer price above $50,000 and up to and including $1,000,000 and 12% of the excess of the hammer price above $1,000,000 and any applicable state or local sales or use tax.
I understand that Christie's provides the service of executing absentee bids for the convenience of clients and that Christie's is not responsible for failing to execute bids or for errors relating to execution of bids. On my behalf, Christie's will try to purchase these lots for the lowest possible price, taking into account the reserve and other bids. Absentee bids submitted on "no reserve" lots will, in the absence of a higher bid, be executed at approximately 50% of the low pre-sale estimate or at the amount of the bid if it is less than 50% of the low pre-sale estimate. If identical absentee bids are received for the same lot, the written bid received first by Christie's will take precedence.
Telephone bids will be accepted for lots with low-end estimates of $1,500 and above, no later than 24 hours prior to the sale and only if the capacity of our pool of staff phone bidders allows. Arrangements to bid in languages other than English must be made well in advance of the sale date.
Telephone bids may be recorded. By bidding on the telephone, prospective purchasers consent to the recording of their conversations. Christie's offers all absentee and telephone bidding services as a convenience to our clients, but will not be responsible for errors or failures to execute bids.
All bids are subject to the terms of the Conditions of Sale and Limited Warranty printed in each Christie's catalogue.

AML 9/9/08

Absentee bids must be received at least 24 hours before the auction begins. Christie's will confirm all bids received by fax by return fax. If you have not received confirmation within one business day, please contact the Bid Department.
Tel: +1 212 636 2437 Fax: +1 212 636 4938 on-line www.christies.com

	2045
Client Number (if applicable)	Sale Number
Billing Name (please print)	
Address	
City State	Zone
Daytime Telephone	Evening Telephone
Fax (Important)	Email

◯ Please tick if you prefer not to receive information about our upcoming sales by e-mail

Signature

If you have not previously bid or consigned with Christie's, please attach copies of the following documents. Individuals: government-issued photo identification (such as a driving licence, national identity card, or passport) and, if not shown on the ID document, proof of current address, for example a utility bill or bank statement. Corporate clients: a certificate of incorporation. Other business structures such as trusts, offshore companies or partnerships: please contact the Credit Department at +1 212 636 2492 for advice on the information you should supply. If you are registering to bid on behalf of someone who has not previously bid or consigned with Christie's, please attach identification documents for yourself as well as the party on whose behalf you are bidding, together with a signed letter of authorization from that party. New clients, clients who have not made a purchase from any Christie's office within the last two years, and those wishing to spend more than on previous occasions will be asked to supply a bank reference. We also request that you complete the section below with your bank details:

Name of Bank(s)

Address of Banks(s)

Account Number(s)

Name of Account Officer(s)

Bank Telephone Number

PLEASE PRINT CLEARLY

Lot number (in numerical order)	Maximum Bid $ (excluding buyer's premium)	Lot number (in numerical order)	Maximum Bid $ (excluding buyer's premium)

Catalogue Subscriptions Order Form

FINE ART

19th Century European Art, American Paintings, Australian Art, German and Austrian Art Impressionist and Modern Art, Italian Sale, Latin American Art, Maritime Paintings and Artefacts, Ottomans and Orientalists, Post-War and Contemporary Art, Swiss Art

Code	Subscription Title	Location	Issues	UK£Price	US$Price	EURPrice
	19th Century European Art					
☐ L193	19th Century European Art	King Street	2	38	61	57
☐ N193	19th Century European Art (includes Orientalists)	New York	3	71	114	108
☐ K193	19th Century European Art	South Kensington	4	57	95	87
☐ A190	19th Century European Art	Amsterdam	2	27	44	40
	American Paintings					
☐ N14	American Paintings	New York & Los Angeles	6	154	257	234
	Australian Art					
☐ L97	Australian Pictures	King Street	1	19	30	29
	Impressionist and Modern Art					
☐ I200	19th and 20th Century Art	Tel Aviv	1	19	30	29
☐ N194	Impressionist and Modern Art	New York	6	171	285	262
☐ K194	Impressionist and Modern Art	South Kensington	2	29	48	44
☐ L194	Impressionist and Modern Art (includes German, Austrian and Surrealist Art)					
		King Street	7	166	266	253
☐ N294	Impressionist and Modern Art, Mid-Season Sales	New York	2	42	67	63
☐ A200	Impressionist, Modern, Post War and Contemporary Art	Amsterdam	2	27	44	40
☐ P194	Impressionist and Modern Art	Paris	2	38	61	57
☐ M200	Modern and Contemporary Art	Milan	2	27	44	40
☐ L191	Orientalists	King Street	1	19	30	29
☐ A201	Pictures, Watercolours and Drawings	Amsterdam	3	40	66	60
☐ K234	Post War and Contemporary Art	South Kensington	2	29	48	44
☐ L347	Post War and Contemporary Art (includes Italian Art)	King Street	9	214	342	325
☐ N347	Post War and Contemporary Art	New York	8	228	380	350
☐ P347	Post War and Contemporary Art	Paris	2	38	61	57
☐ L361	Russian Pictures	King Street	2	48	76	72
☐ M207	Spanish Art	Madrid	1	19	30	29
☐ C110	Swiss Art	Zurich	2	32	53	49
	Latin American Art					
☐ N84	Latin American Art	New York	2	51	86	78

Catalogue Subscriptions Order Form

Billing Address/Send catalogues to:

Name

Address

Daytime Telephone   Facsimile   e-mail

◯ Please tick if you prefer not to receive information about our upcoming sales by e-mail

Christie's Client Number

Method of payment: ◯ Visa ◯ MasterCard ◯ American Express

Card Number   Expiry Date

Card Member Signature

Cheque enclosed US$ UK£ EUR Please make cheque payable to Christie's

Residents of the US states of CA, CT, DC, FL, IL, MA, NJ, NY, PA, RI, and TX please add local sales tax.
Residents of Belgium, France, Germany, Italy, the Netherlands, and Spain please add local VAT. Tax Exempt clients must include a copy of their Tax Exempt Certificate.
Orders shipped to North or South America will be charged in US dollars. Orders shipped to the European Union (except the UK) will be charged in euros. All other orders will be charged in UK pounds sterling.

Receive beautifully illustrated catalogues from our auctions around the world.
Your private view of some of the world's most beautiful objects and an indispensable guide to forth-coming auctions will be mailed to you as soon as available.

To place an order: please indicate your choice above and complete your details on the left and fax or mail this form. Alternatively, view catalogues free online at christies.com.

Reply to:

Christie's Catalogues, 8 King Street, St James's
London SW1Y 6QT, United Kingdom
Tel: +44 (0)20 7389 2820 Fax: +44 (0)20 7389 2869
subscribe-uk@christies.com

Christie's Catalogues, 20 Rockefeller Plaza
New York, NY 10020, USA
Tel: +1 800 395 6300   Fax: +1 800 395 5600
From outside US
Tel: +1 212 636 2500   Fax: +1 212 636 4940
subscribe-us@christies.com

CHRISTIE'S

CHRISTIE'S

10/03/08

Printed in England by
© Christie, Manson & Woods Ltd. (2008)
Creative Director: Martin Schott, Christie's Creative Services, NY
Catalogue photo credits: Chew Ho, John Parnell, Reid Baker,
Stephen Arnold, and Matthew Marston